THE GREAT
NORTH EAST
BREWERY
GUIDE

cheers

"BEER DESERVES TO BE
TREATED AS A CIVILISED
DRINK; IT MAY EVEN HAVE
BEEN THE CAUSE OF
CIVILISATION"

- MICHAEL JACKSON
BEER AND WHISKY WRITER

CONTENTS

FOREWORD

Terry Laybourne, chef and owner of 21 Hospitality Group,
operator of The Broad Chare, Newcastle

Craft beer has a long and rich history, but it's fair to say there has been an explosion in activity and interest in the last decade with consumers thankfully shifting from bland, mass-manufactured beer brands towards craft breweries making distinctive, speciality beers.

The best of our regional breweries understand great brewing technique, fusing traditional skills with modern innovation. They appreciate multiple flavour profiles, often using non-traditional hops along with other aromatic ingredients.

Often the real secret to a good glass of beer is down to the restraint exercised by the brewer. The better small independent breweries focus on the balance of flavour and create beer of great subtlety. This broad flavour spectrum within good beers allows us to match them well with food. It's here we see some common traits with the best of our region's chefs, who acknowledge the value of local produce and good, balanced flavours.

When creating our house beer, The Writer's Block, for The Broad Chare, the challenge was to design an ale with cleansing properties and enough character to handle the fattiness we all love in bar snacks like pork pies and Scotch eggs.

We should champion the best of our breweries, where people are putting their own personality and love into their beer. This all adds real character to our region's identity. Long may they flourish and continue to innovate.

offstone

Published by Offstone Publishing,
Bearl Farm, Stocksfield, Northumberland NE43 7AL
Email: enquiries@offstonepublishing.co.uk
Website: www.offstonepublishing.co.uk
Twitter: @offstonepublish

Publishers: Jane Pikett, Gary Ramsay
Editor: Alastair Gilmour
Design: Mark Carr
Photography: Peter Skelton
Project Management: Emma Howe

First published: 2017   **ISBN:** 978-1-5272-1647-1   **Printed by:** Stephens & George Print Group

WELCOME

Alastair Gilmour, editor, Cheers

Alastair Gilmour

People talk about gardeners having green fingers, but it's a description that could readily be applied to brewers. Leek growers rear their plants like their children, dahlia experts talk to their blooms, and carrots don't perform unless their rosettes are fondled regularly. It's the same with beer, it has to be treated with devotion at every stage.

Brew it from the finest ingredients possible on the best equipment available with heaps of inventive muscle and brains and the results will speak for themselves. Craft brewers are fanatical about their choice of hops, the malt they order, the mashing-in regime, the conditioning, the ageing and attention to every detail. It's what makes great beer – and here in the North East of England we have some of the most inventive, knowledgeable and skilful brewers in the nation, working on gleaming kit that wouldn't look out of place in a sci-fi movie.

Our breweries range from cramped units such as shipping containers to huge and impressive structures lined with Italian marble. The process of making beer is much the same in all of them and honesty and flamboyance come out at the other end, which is beer's beauty. The region's brewers are a dedicated lot, a set of charismatic people with individual traits that influence the beer they brew. And we don't half brew good beer here, which is what this book celebrates.

There are now more than 2,000 breweries operating in the UK, representing a growth rate over the past five years of 64%. The North East has enjoyed a similar percentage rise in craft brewery start-ups, many of them by former home-brewers inspired by a public demand for adventurous flavours and the realisation that now is the time.

We're all reaping the benefit of better quality beer and more choice, plus the altruistic notion that we're in our small way contributing to a fiercely independent movement and doing our bit for the growth of the local economy.

Beer can be as simple or as sophisticated as we wish it to be. Breweries produce it, but never forget, it's people who make it and people who drink it. Cheers!

ALLENDALE
BREWERY

ALLENDALE BREWERY

EST. 2006
WWW.ALLENDALEBREWERY.COM

If ever there was a monument to stainless steel, it's right there in the shimmering flesh of Allendale Brewery. Dominating the brewhouse are 13, 20-barrel fermentation tanks, each of them weighing around four tonnes when full. It's an extraordinary sight that must impress every one of the staff on the start of every shift – and that's before a host of other sparkling brewing vessels is taken into consideration.

Allendale Brewery was founded in 2006 in a stone-built, slate-roofed Victorian lead smelting mill in the rugged North Pennines – what naturalist Dr David Bellamy described as England's last wilderness.

Reflecting the area's stark beauty and industrial heritage has been the aim since Valentine's Day 2006, when Tom Hick and his father Jim set out on their brewing odyssey. Tom now holds the reins along with wife Lucy while being prompted and prodded by hugely talented brewer and former chef Neil Thomas and a team with a

Owners and brewers Tom and Lucy Hick with head brewer Neil Thomas and the Allendale Brewery team

Rick Lee, brewer

passion for great beer. Allendale's roots are in brewing cask ale for the local market and it has built a reputation for quality, consistent beer in keg, bottle and, more recently, can as well as cask.

Moving with the times, a changing and challenging market, and anticipating flavour profiles has become more acute than ever, but Allendale is well up for it.

For instance, drinkers new to craft beer tend to like cans, so there's quite a lot of focus on that area with Wayfarer Pale Ale (4.4% abv) and Wilderness IPA (6.5% abv) now available across the north, including 150 Morrisons stores.

A diverse range takes careful note and inspiration from the best of British, European and New World ingredients and styles

This approach has also seen the Co-op come knocking, while own brands are produced for Marks & Spencer; the capacity allowing the company to explore other areas. But Allendale still retains a small brewery feel achieved via a five-barrel test kit used to brew speciality beers for pub chains, unique brews, "crazy" one-offs, short runs, and for kegging. This is also where the End series of special beers sees the light of day.

The brewery's belief is that flavours should be in balance, with ingredients allowed to do the job they've been selected for while also leaving room for experiment. A diverse range takes careful note and inspiration from the best of British, European and New World ingredients and styles, resulting in a wall of accolades from the Campaign For Real Ale (CAMRA), the Society of Independent Brewers (SIBA), Great Taste, and the pinnacle – half a dozen World Beer Awards with, in particular, gold medals for APA (5.5% abv), Adder Lager (5.0% abv) and Pennine Pale (4.0% abv) which also runs Golden Plover (4.0% abv) close for best-seller status.

There's always another area to explore and Allendale has been brewing beer for the Danish market, with Insane Darkness Imperial Stout (8.4% abv) and Immortal Viking DIPA (8.2% abv) particularly well received around Copenhagen.

Allendale Brewery might be set in the North Pennines, but there's definitely nothing remote about its vision and inspiration. Plus, there's a lot of Wilderness around.

ALLEN MILL, ALLENDALE, HEXHAM NORTHUMBERLAND, NE47 9EA
📞 **01434 618 686**
📘 **@allendale.brewery**
🐦 **@allendaleale**

ALMASTY BREWING CO.

EST. AUGUST 2014
WWW.ALMASTY.CO.UK

> ## "
> *The only constant for Almasty appears to be change*

When you name your brewery in honour of a wild tribe covered in long brown hair you get the notion there may be something different at play. The Almas are thought to exist in Central Asia and Russia but, like the Yeti, no specimen exists. Yet.

There is certainly something different going on at Shiremoor-based Almasty Brewing Co with beers such as Peanut Butter Porter (5.0% abv), Oats & Milk (4.8% abv) and Lilt Pale Ale (5.0% abv) demonstrating that owner Mark McGarry and his team take an ever-inventive and innovative approach to brewing. Mark McGarry learned his brewing skills at Mordue and Tyne Bank breweries, but had been developing his knowledge as a peripatetic cook working across Europe, Canada and New Zealand, which he says helped his understanding of ingredients and how flavours compare and diverge. A high tech approach to brewing contradicts Almasty's homespun pumpclips – thin slices of wood, each 100mm in diameter, printed with all one needs to know when ordering something special. Long lengths of slender, straight tree trunks sit in one corner of the brewhouse waiting for a band saw and an accurate eye.

Wood is actually a significant feature at Almasty – an education in how Imperial Stouts, lambics and other sour beers age over a year in former wine and bourbon casks.

Almasty exists to explore – the ten-barrel brewery was an early adopter of canned beer and racy graphics – while also bringing that sense of adventure to its beers through different techniques and unexplored styles. Then what has been learned goes forward into the next recipe and the next, particularly from hop varieties and their combinations that draw out massive flavours and aromas. This approach developed the likes of American Brown (5.8% abv), Smoking Gun (4.6% abv) and Oyster & Seaweed Porter (5.0% abv) among countless others.

It's a conundrum facing most brewers – do you press on with a range of well-received core beers brewed constantly week-in, week-out, which you daren't tamper with, or freewheel with something more experimental creating uncompromising big, bold flavours, seasonally inspired beers – and fun. Collaborations and brewery open days have encouraged the team to think about how to improve on what is already there.

Luckily for us, the only constant for Almasty appears to be change.

UNIT 11, ALGERNON INDUSTRIAL ESTATE, NEWCASTLE UPON TYNE NE27 0NB
☎ 0191 253 1639
f @AlmastyBrewCo
🐦 @AlmastyBrewCo
📷 @almastybrewingco

ANTI-VENOM IPA

ANARCHY BREW CO.

EST. JANUARY 2012
WWW.ANARCHYBREWCO.COM

Huge images of beer labels are pinned around the walls at Anarchy Brewery. They're not just space-fillers to brighten up the Morpeth, Northumberland, visitor centre and brewhouse, but reminders that here is a centre of excellence and a home of pride, passion and spirit. They shout "this is what we make".

The images work equally well with customers and staff – in-your-face billboards that the casual viewer can't ignore and chest-puffing sources of pride in doing what they do.

Anarchy Brew Co started life in January 2012 as Brew Star, but difficulties with the name of another brewery emerged, forcing owners Simon and Dawn Miles to re-think. But problem turned to opportunity; it gave them time to reflect on what they had learned and to reconsider the whole direction of the business.

Anarchy has expanded every year and still can't fulfil demand. The brewery was founded

ANARCHY
BREW CO
XMAS CHAOS
4.3% RUM RAISIN PORTER
ABV

@ANARCHYBREWCO

ANARCHY BREW
URBAN
ASSAULT
AMERICAN PALE ALE

WORLD BEER AWARDS

5.0

Simon and Dawn Miles with the Anarchy Brew Co. team

> ## "
> *If you always do what you've always done, you'll always have what you've always had*

to concentrate on big flavours, so its range started dramatically, concentrating on the boldness of citrus-soaked session beers, kiwi fruit and lime-loaded IPAs and coffee-infused stouts.

More than 20 distinctly different and increasingly forward-looking beers are produced which include Blonde Star (4.1% abv), a well-loved blonde beer, Boot Boys (5.0% abv), a classic northern brown ale, and Citra Star (4.1% abv) which comes loaded with grapefruit, lemon and lime flavours.

Anarchy Brew Co. has also gained recognition at the World Beer Awards as Urban Assault (5.0% abv) was voted the UK's Best Pale Ale in 2017; Sublime Chaos (7% abv) was voted Best Stout in the UK and Europe in 2015, and AntiVenom was voted Best IPA in the UK in 2017.

Simon Miles is also keen to do more one-off showcase beers such as wheat beers, gluten-free, vegan-friendly and unfiltered, and the Anarchy set up with its two sets of brewing kit – one that keeps regular beers flowing and the other for creating new products – is perfectly suited for that. And it's more fun that way.

Brewing equipment, with its ten conditioning tanks and a whirlpool that clarifies the wort, is run off its feet preparing beer for cask, keg and can. An export strategy puts extra demand on the brewery with shipments of beer going all over the globe, including Russia, France, Italy, Spain, Scandinavia and soon America, China, and Japan.

One key aspect to Anarchy's success – apart from the beer – is its branding developed by Newcastle design company Dirty Hands. The strongest idea that emerged through meetings, storyboards and staff involvement was that the imagery should have a Punk, DIY aesthetic. This was achieved using newspaper-style typography involving headlines, intros, cross-heads and cut-and-paste torn-up lettering.

The wording might fade, smudge and dance in and out of focus, but it emphasises what Johnny Rotten sang: "Cause I wanna be... Anarchy".

WHITEHOUSE FARM CENTRE
MORPETH, NORTHUMBERLAND
NE61 6AW
📞 **01670 789 755**
f **@anarchybrewco**
🐦 **@anarchybrewco**
📷 **@anarchybrewco**

AUTUMN BREWING CO.

AUTUMN BREWING CO.

EST. SEPTEMBER 2015
WWW.AUTUMNBREWING.CO.UK

Autumn Brewing Co is proud of its firsts; the first brewing company to brew all of its beers and lagers domestically in the UK using only naturally gluten-free brewing malts and quinoa; the first in the UK to import Eckert Malting & Brewing Company's gluten-free rice brewing malts; the first in the UK and Europe to import Grouse Malt House naturally gluten-free millet brewing malts for commercial use.

Autumn Brewing Co was set up by former Greggs employee Peter Briggs to produce gluten-free beers for people with allergies to wheat, barley and rye, coeliac disease or gluten sensitivities. ALT BREW (ALTernative BREWing), a range of Coeliac UK-certified gluten-free bottled and kegged craft beers and lagers, were developed as part of a comprehensive R&D programme in conjunction with Brewlab, the Sunderland based brewery training and analysis company.

After a start-up brewing course at Brewlab, Sunerland, Peter investigated the viability of the gluten-free beer market, and worked on formulating recipes throughout the first half of 2016. The beer styles that ultimately developed were ALT BREW NO.01 Bavarian-style Pilsner; ALT BREW NO.02 traditional English Pale Ale, and ALT BREW NO.03

All our beers are brewed using only naturally gluten-free grains and brewing malts

Dark Roast Stout. The beers are designed to appeal to consumers, whether they observe a gluten-free lifestyle or are looking for great beers made from alternative grains such as rice, millet and quinoa rather than mainstream barley-based beers. For those who follow a gluten-free diet, either out of necessity or choice, finding great-tasting beers brewed from naturally gluten-free ingredients is a real joy.

And joy certainly came Autumn Brewing Co's way after only two months of trading when its ALT BEW NO.01 Pilsner was presented with a silver medal at the FreeFrom Food Awards 2017. Further recognition followed in October 2017 with a Highly Commended in the national Beer and Cider Marketing Awards. Peter Briggs was joined in April 2017 by former Formica Group employee John Chilton and the guys are particularly proud of their Dark Roast Stout - the first stout to be brewed in the UK using only naturally gluten-free grains. Autumn Brewing Co continues to champion and raise awareness of gluten-free beers for people who are allergic to wheat, barley and rye, or are diagnosed with coeliac disease.

8 EAST CLIFF ROAD, SPECTRUM BUSINESS PARK, SEAHAM COUNTY DURHAM, SR7 7PS
📞 0191 581 0751
f @autumnbrewingco
🐦 @autumnbrewingco
📷 @autumnbrewing

BEACON BRAUHAUS EST. JUNE 2016

When you name your first beer after a song with the lyrics "I'm all right where I am", it suggests a certain level of brewing confidence. Lady Eleanor Elderflower Pale Ale, the inaugural beer from Beacon Brauhaus "pico-brewery", was launched in 2016 at the newly-unveiled Lindisfarne Festival, which was appropriate, given that North East folk-rock legends Lindisfarne were on stage at the time and included Alan Hull's 1971 song in their set.

Brewery owner Marcus Hahn, originally from Dortmund in Germany – a city with a proud brewing tradition – launched Beacon Brauhaus on Holy Island (aka Lindisfarne) in June 2016, the first on the tidal island for 500 years. His family had enjoyed annual holidays on Holy Island from 2000, eventually settling there. Marcus had been home brewing for a year, he is completely self-taught, learning from brewing books and YouTube.

Following positive feedback from the Lindisfarne gig and brewing exclusively for Pilgrims Coffee House on Holy Island, where the kitchen doubled as the brewery, Marcus received an invitation to take Lady Eleanor (4.3% abv) to the CAMRA Darlington Beer Festival where it had another hit outing. Still not sure how to capitalise on his skills, he enrolled on a script-writing and drama course at Northumbria University, although he really wanted to study film. After a year he decided it wasn't for him and settled into catering and cooking, which gave him a solid grounding in brewing beer, which he equates to creating a delicious stew or flavourful sauce.

He was brewing more than enough to keep Pilgrims Coffee House stocked with an expanding range that includes Jigsaw American Amber (5.4% abv) and Nightcrawler Porter (4.9% abv), but demand outstripped capacity and the kitchen-brewery was frequently overrun with activity. While delivering beer to Berwick, he mentioned to the owners of the Brown Bear Inn that he had tried and failed to find suitable brewery premises on Holy Island. The conversation went something like: "You've got the space, I need the space".

Brewing started in the recently revitalised pub in November 2017 following a major upgrade in equipment. Marcus pulls pints between producing 120 litres (two casks) at a time, which is a mutually beneficial arrangement. Eventually, he'll brew some German-influenced beers, but for the moment he's concentrating on his real ale passion. He's all right where he is.

> "
> *Give a man a beer and waste an hour. Teach a man to brew and waste a lifetime - Bill Owen*

27 HIDE HILL
BERWICK-UPON-TWEED
NORTHUMBERLAND, TD15 1EQ
📞 07711 924 365
📘 @beaconbrauhaus
📷 @beaconbrauhaus

21

Ross Holland

Box Social Brewing

EST. 2015
WWW.BOXSOCIAL.PUB

It's often said that a week is a long time in politics because so much can happen in a short space of time. In similar fashion, two years in brewing has flown by for Box Social Brewing and more happened in those 24 months than father and son owners Steve and Ross Holland could have ever dared dream.

Newburn, Newcastle-based Box Social Brewing has hardly had time to sit back and enjoy the progress. First, it produced a fine core range of beers with enormous amounts of research and development thrown in, then experimental beers that took off despite – or due to – making full use of unconventional and non-traditional ingredients. A bespoke beer for Tygers Of Pan Tang, the heavy metal band that never seems to stop touring, sold particularly well (followed by version two) and a tap house – The Box Social – was opened in Newcastle city centre.

A toe-dipping exercise into exporting has reaped benefits, new branding has come on stream and expansion plans are moving at

Ross and Steve Holland

a pace after new premises were secured to cope with ambitious growth plans.

A box social is a Victorian term for a social event where guests bring food and drink to swap among themselves in stimulating, sociable company. Curiously, they tended to be sober affairs with no alcohol involved. If this sounds all very relaxed and easy-going, Box Social drives a relentless production regime in its search for ever-more beer styles.

Box Social Brewing is the realisation of a dream for Ross, an accomplished home-brewer, and former fireman Steve, who has refurbished a fire engine fully equipped with six keg lines to dispense craft beer and even prosecco. Although Ross knew the basics inside out, he and Steve took a three-day start-up course at Brewlab training centre in Sunderland.

The six-barrel brewery vessels were bought from a variety of sources, including from Cornwall and from Ringway Brewery in Stockport, which is owned by a Geordie with a penchant for black and white casks. The brewery launched its first beer on May 15, 2015 at the Crown Posada in Newcastle.

There was a marked difference between Box Social's first and second years – starting from scratch you have to develop

your product range, introduce it to the marketplace, and gain the confidence of customers, let alone get used to the peculiarities of new brewing vessels. For Box Social, year two was about producing more experimental beers which have been a big help to the business.

Fortunately, one of their first beers was Gentlemen's Nectar (4.2% abv), an American-style pale ale with tropical fruit to the fore that caught the public imagination and stimulated tastebuds. It remains a best seller. Ross Holland admits that production of Gentlemen's Nectar could be a full-time operation, given its popularity, as it "keeps the lights on" and everything else is a bonus.

The decision to move premises was prompted by the simple fact that Box Social continuously sold out of beer at a remarkable rate. The next challenge is to continue business growth and production, which involves installing its own kegging and canning facility. Box Social beers in cans are now massively outselling bottled beer (which they thought were doing well) as customers turn on to their ease of use and guarantee of freshness. This also leads to bigger volumes so beer can be sold all over the country. The

> **We only brew beers that we like to drink. Flavour is the key**

crisp and floral Kaffir Lime Leaf Session IPA (4.3% abv). The 2016 collaboration with Tygers Of Pan Tang resulted in Tyger Blood (5.0% abv), which was followed six months later by a more heavily hopped second edition Tyger Blood V2 (5.5% abv). It's said the first version sold "stupidly well" during the course of a British tour that started in The Cluny in Newcastle with the launch of a new album.

Tyger Blood is a red ale that traditionally comes with a well-balanced hop and malt character. It's an easy-drinking beer full of caramel and toasted notes. Red ales are popular in Ireland with versions brewed in Belgium and a further variant making US drinkers sit up.

Expansion in personnel is yet another positive development with Roger Cowgill joining the team – a brilliant home-brewer, apparently, and an expert in Belgian beer styles with a deep knowledge of wild yeasts as alternatives to those cultured in a lab. He selects samples from the local dene to assess their effects on fermentation which should add another dimension to the Box Social offer.

The tough regime of seven-day weeks have paid off for Ross and Steve Holland; the fire engine is on standby, the heat is on and there are thirsts to be doused.

original unit will remain for experimental brews, as a tasting room and for maturing barrel-aged beers.

One unexpected spin-off from having their own pub is that it acts as a shop window where local landlords frequently try Box Social beers and invariably like them so much they order them for their own places. For instance, Campfire Porter (7.0% abv) has customers crying out for it and has been added to the core range which, at that sort of strength and full-on flavour, came as a bit of a surprise.

Other Box Social beers include Real Facemelter (3.9% abv), Inner City Sumo DDH IPA (6.6% abv), Bad Medicine 60-Minute IPA (6.0% abv), Sticky Beak American Pale Ale (4.2% abv), Sky & Thunders Zeus Sour (3.7% abv) and the

UNITS 1-3, WINNINGS COURTYARD NEWBURN, NEWCASTLE UPON TYNE NE15 9RU
📞 **0191 267 1295**
@BoxSocialBrewing
@boxsocialbeer
@BoxSocialBrewing

BRINKBURN ST.

EST. JANUARY 2015
WWW.BRINKBURNBREWERY.CO.UK

Brewing vessels clad in black and white stripes and the strapline 'Born and Brewed in Byker' are two clues to where one brewery's heart lies. Brinkburn St Brewery, now located at the original Maling Pottery factory on Hume Street in the Ouseburn Valley, couldn't be more at home in Newcastle if it tried.

Started in January 2015 by engineer Lee Renforth, Brinkburn St made its first beer, The Pursuit of Hoppiness v1 (5.9% abv) - a west coast juicy and hazy hop bomb with loads of Amarillo and Citra - in May 2015 in collaboration with Magic Rock. Since, it has brewed 35 more beers, with 15 of these now included in its core beer range. Involving the right people from the start has been crucial, such as former Pheonix head brewer Richard Bazen, highly respected within the brewing industry and holder of a number of champion beer awards, who has brought more than 30 years' experience to the brewery.

On the same wavelength are brewer Stew Southern, Lee Dolman (operations), Josie Smith (sales and comms), Jude Bazen (account manager), and Natasha Allen (trainee brewer). Visitors need only spend five minutes in the brewhouse to understand how much the team love the unique and historical Ouseburn Valley and how proud they are to be a part of it. There are plans for a taproom and kitchen alongside the brewery in the 200-year old Maling Pottery building that was one of Britain's first workers' schools, whilst a WWII air-raid shelter tunnel in the building is being earmarked for barrel ageing. The brewery is also being upgraded with additional fermentation vessels to double the production capability of the 8-barrel kit.

Brinkburn St prides itself on brewing beer for all of the people, by some of the people, and brews a wide range of beers including Groovy Juice, a New England IPA; Geordie Pagoda II, a Sorachi and Azacca pale ale; The Pursuit of Hoppiness 2017, a citrus and stone fruit IPA; Tyne Titans Session IPA, a fruity IPA; and Homage to Mesopotamia, a unique porter with late additions of Shiraz grapes and honey.

Brinkburn St brings worldie craft and old-fashioned graft to every new brew with a beer range inspired from around both the modern and ancient worlds.

There's beauty in what they do; you can taste it.

> ❝ We brew a wide range of inclusive beer for all of the people, brewed by some of the people

QUAYSIDE I4, OUSEBURN BUILDING ALBION ROW, NEWCASTLE UPON TYNE, NE6 1LL

📞 0191 260 0688
f @brinkburnstreetbrewery
🐦 @brinkburnstbrew
📷 @brinkburn_street

ESTD 1865

CAMERONS
·THE NORTH EAST BREWERS·

CAMERONS BREWERY

EST. 1865
WWW.CAMERONSBREWERY.COM

In the year that the first speed limit was introduced by the Locomotive Act – 2mph in towns and 4mph in the country – John William Cameron was starting a new job in West Hartlepool. There's no doubt he wouldn't have been the only one seeking new employment in 1865, but this young man had quite a bit to offer his Lion Brewery employers, having served an apprenticeship as a brewer and maltster.

Like the steam trains of the day, John's career quickly picked up speed and he assumed

control of the Lion Brewery in 1872. A North East success story, spanning to date more than 150 years, had begun.

Today, Camerons is not only an influential force in the North East of England, but through national distribution of its ales, a programme of contract brewing, and an approach that combines innovation, enterprise and initiative, it is rightly recognised as one of Britain's great beer producers.

Camerons has always recognised that the only direction was investment in quality

personnel, high tech plant, equipment, infrastructure and the best of raw materials. Now competition is from the nationals, other regionals and quality microbreweries which have given the brewing sector a 21st Century jolt.

Time and again over its history, Camerons was passed around owners such as shipping giant Ellerman Lines, Brent Walker – which also owned 1,200 William Hill betting shops – and the secretive Barclay brothers of The Ritz Hotel, The Daily Telegraph, the Channel Island Brecqhou, and Wolverhampton & Dudley Breweries.

Come 2002, in stepped David Soley, owner of Castle Eden Brewery, which he had bought from Whitbread in 1998. Today, Camerons Brewery is one of the largest private breweries in the UK, with the capacity to produce more than 1 million hectolitres of beer annually.

As well as brewing its own high quality beers and lagers, including its flagship beer Strongarm, the well-rounded 4.0% abv Ruby Red Ale, and the Motörhead collaboration Röad Crew American IPA, Camerons is a major contract brewer for the likes of Heineken and Carlsberg, as well as other major multinational companies.

In addition to its core brewing operation, Camerons possesses a growing retail pub estate of more than 70 venues ranging from community pubs and city centre venues, to restaurant and accommodation-based outlets. This includes the popular Head of Steam brand, which the firm acquired in 2014, and seven new pubs purchased from Leeds Brewery in July 2016.

The addition of the Head of Steam group of pubs in Newcastle, Gateshead, Durham, Huddersfield, Sheffield, Tynemouth, Liverpool, Hull and Leeds is a major boost. Head of Steam outlets have retained their individual style and offbeat character; managers and staff know their customers better than anybody in the licensed trade.

The brewery Visitor Centre is located nearby on the site of the Stranton pub – one of Hartlepool's oldest – where visiting groups begin brewery tours with a series of interactive visual displays and pub games then end in traditional fashion at the brewery tap.

The Italian marble-lined and decorative wrought-iron brew hall are sights guaranteed to take the breath away, while business-wise, the brewery offers Hartlepool and the surrounding area three meeting rooms for conferences and private functions. Souvenirs

> " *The Italian marble-lined and decorative wrought-iron brew hall are sights guaranteed to take the breath away*

band's fans' favourite track (We Are) The Road Crew, from the 1980s Ace of Spades album. With lines like "Another beer is what I need" the name is the perfect fit for an American-style pale ale.

But it wouldn't be a Camerons' story without a word or two about the legendary Strongarm (4.0% abv), which came along in 1955, originally advertised as "the strongest ale on Teesside at 1/7d per pint". Its nickname, The Ruby Red, emphasises its handsome colour. It is rich and toffee malty with a seesaw of sweetness and bitterness that might tip towards the former, but still manages to create an all-round balance. Hop varieties are workhorse Fuggles, Target and Goldings, while Pale Ale and Crystal malts create the colour and the grainy base.

Brewery-wise, Camerons has embarked on its biggest single capital investment since a major expansion in 2008 – a total of £1.5m on a brand-new purpose-built bottling line capable of operating at 10,000 units per hour, providing the company with a complete vertically integrated, cost-effective business.

In 1865 – the days of John William Cameron – local newspapers were advertising Widow Welch's Female Pills "celebrated for removing giddiness and eminently useful in wind disorders".

Camerons has reached giddy heights and will remain there, and there's still a lot more to achieve.

are always a great reminder of a different day out, and The History of the Lion Brewery by Marie-Louise McKay is a fascinating 96-page appreciation of more than 150 years of brewing at the iconic site.

Brewery upgrades and product rebranding are part of a rolling programme along with a huge expansion in the production of seasonal and special ales such as Fridge Magnet (4.5% abv), Brown Dog (4.3%) and Thirst Blood (4.3%) to complement the core cask offer of Strongarm (4.0%), A-hop-alypse Now (4.3%), Röad Crew (4.5%) and keg brands Trophy Special (4.0%), Steamer Smooth (3.8%) and Monkey Stout (4.0%).

Camerons has also been hard at work producing a range of craft ales which include Black Forest Gateaux Porter (5.5%), Sleeping BrewTea (4.4%) and Tontine Milk Stout (4.1%).

Röad Crew APA (4.5% keg/cask 5.0% abv bottle) forms a key part of the brewery's developing brand range. The beer, which has been brewed in collaboration with legendary UK rock band Motörhead, was named after the

LION BREWERY, HARTLEPOOL
COUNTY DURHAM, TS24 7QS
📞 **01429 852 000**
📘 @CameronsBrewery
🐦 @CameronsBrewery
📷 @camerons_brewery

CONSETT ALE WORKS

EST. APRIL 2016
WWW.CONSETTALEWORKS.CO.UK

A brewery that links Blackpool Tower and Britain's fleet of nuclear submarines could easily form part of a pub quiz. But a question about the mutual connection might be followed by bouts of head-scratching and a spot of subversive googling.

Consett Ale Works, situated in former stables behind the Grey Horse pub in the town, brews beers with names that lean heavily on the long-gone Consett Iron

Company (later Consett Steel Works) and its nostalgia-steeped references. It's where the steel was made that constructed the iconic seaside visitor attraction and our ultimate defence capability.

Steel Town Bitter and White Hot refer to "The Company" as it was known locally, while Red Dust recalls Consett's infamous blanket of iron oxide that covered the whole town and coloured the sky until its closure in 1980 with the loss of 3,700 jobs. This created an unemployment rate of 35%

destroying a vibrant community. Entrepreneur Jeff Hind bought the Grey Horse and its brewing facility – originally Derwent Rose Brewery – in 2006. A new floor was laid, efficient drainage was installed along with all the painting, cladding, tiling, three-phase electricity and half a dozen stainless steel vessels that not only represent a five-barrel production capacity, but another serious business venture in the Hind portfolio.

Jeff Hind, who owns several pubs scattered around the North East, has decades of experience in the hospitality sector, but even he was surprised by the immediate success of Consett Ale Works' first brews. He and head brewer Rufus Thompson worked with Hadrian Border Brewery owner Andy Burrows at every stage in development until everybody was as comfortable with hydrometers and sparging as they were with darts and dominoes. Rufus also studied at Brewlab training centre in Sunderland, with whom he keeps in close contact when creating new beers.

Jeff Hind worked through his business plan with the former Derwentside District Council (now absorbed by Durham County Council's Business Durham team)

outlining the projections and the finances that would access the funding to match his own investment, which then enabled him to purchase brewing equipment. Then he sat down with anyone who would listen to decide what the beers should taste like, what they should look like, and what sort of range and strength they should go for while gradually narrowing down the ingredients that would achieve those characteristics.

Grey Horse customers were also invited to suggest the name for the brewery and his email inbox was virtually overwhelmed by suggestions. Consett Ale Works came out a clear winner.

Steel Town Bitter (3.8% abv), a quaffing ale and an entry point for lager drinkers, has a good mid-range colour; it's hoppy and rather sweet to begin with, but a pleasant malt influence eventually surfaces.

Red Dust (4.5% abv) is ruby red in colour and beautifully clear with a robust, full-flavoured malt and fruit nature.

Cast Iron (4.1% abv) is a light ale with a surprisingly sharp aftertaste, while White Hot (4.0% abv), is the perfect summer beer; highly hopped and sparkling with

> " *The brewhouse is being expanded into next door, set to double the space for brewing three and four times a week*

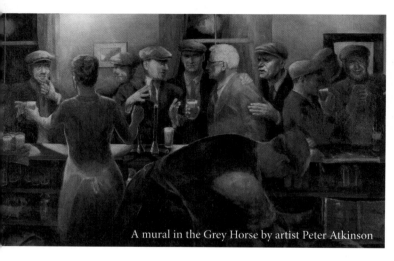

A mural in the Grey Horse by artist Peter Atkinson

and four times a week. The brewing capacity remains at five barrels, a conscious decision that protects the brewery's boutique and bespoke nature. Beers get swallowed up by the Grey Horse and its sister pubs, and a fair amount goes out into the North East trade to the Sir John Fitzgerald group, the Head of Steam group, and Camerons' pub estate.

Mindful of the local identity in every brew, Consett Ale Works is set for a rebranding during 2018 to promote the Steel Town tradition, heritage, history and working folks' culture. Like the brewery, it will represent solidity and passion and should be easy to recognise on a bar crowded with pumpclips.

A mural in the Grey Horse bar depicts that culture, with steel workers portrayed in a moment of relaxation slaking their thirsts before returning to work on their respective shifts the following day.

Artist Peter Atkinson studiously delved into books and illustrations on how people in County Durham would have looked and dressed at a particular point in history. He also painted a similarly striking work for the Beamish Mary pub – CAMRA national pub of the year in 1995 and a sister enterprise to Consett Ale Works.

Grey Horse customers are loyal and discerning and have a deep understanding of their history, where they've come from and how Consett was formed. Consett Ale Works devotees know their beer, and that's a cast-iron certainty.

115 SHERBURN TERRACE
CONSETT, COUNTY DURHAM
DH8 6NE
📞 **01207 591 540 / 07778 220 214**

wheat-like cereal characteristics. Like other Consett Ale Works beers, it has excellent head retention.

Jeff Hind is something of a collector of down to earth pubs. He owns the Beamish Mary at No Place and The Square & Compass at West Cornforth – both in County Durham – and The Salutation in Billingham, Teesside - all of them real ale outlets. He reasons that he likes traditional drinking pubs full of characters that have cask ales and huge fireplaces.

The Grey Horse dates from 1846 and was previously known as the Target Inn. It's a real locals' pub where regulars come from either down the road or a dozen miles away, most of them drawn by the six cask-conditioned ales on offer. At one time, the pub even had a regular customer from the Isle of Man, seduced by Consett Ale Works' flavours and aromas.

The brewhouse is being expanded into the unit next door and a new cellar is set to double the space to cope with brewing three

⊙ CREDENCE

CREDENCE BREWING

EST. 2015
WWW.CREDENCEBREWING.CO.UK

> **Credence:
> Believe in beer**

The Neolithic rock art that decorates the moors of Northumberland inspired the Credence team in their beauty and craft, defining the region while at the same time linking it to other regions of cultural excellence. The Credence brand should be seen as a kite mark of Northumbrian quality following in the footsteps of these ancient cup-and-ring marks.

Credence is based in the heart of one of Britain's friendliest ports, Amble. It was here, in 2015, that Credence rolled the first barrels out of its 10-barrel custom-built brew house. Amble is a great place to be involved in the food and drink industry right now and has a fine offering of new restaurants and bars.

Two years on, the brewery has developed a solid reputation for producing great tasting and highly sessionable beer. Fermentation capacity has increased from 10 barrels a week to 40 barrels, meaning the brewery can keep favourites in stock whilst creating new and exciting products.

Credence now offers products in a range of packaging options, with bottles, kegs and casks all brewed and packaged in-house. The introduction of keg and bottles to the Credence product range has allowed the brewery to explore and enter markets further afield.

Business manager Callum Burns says: "We are excited about working with new customers, both nationally and internationally and to see where our beers will end up over the next few years."

The latest Credence adventure is the introduction of the barrel-ageing program. After sourcing a collection of stunning French wine barrels, they plan to age some of their finest 'one-off' special brews in them – so keep an eye out for these unique limited editions. These will be available from the brewery and online shop, allowing you to enjoy Credence beer fresh from the source or delivered fresh to your door.

Beers include Credence Porter (4.4% abv), a homage to malt with no fewer than 11 varieties of barley, rye and wheat blended for a smooth, robust mouth feel. White Session IPA (4.8% abv) delivers intricate pine, grapefruit and stone fruit notes from American hops, alongside wheat and German malts which add complexity and balance to the body. Credence Blonde (4.0% abv) combines a Northumbrian heritage malt base with German Pils malts while Cascade hops add refreshing floral and citrus notes. Elemental IPA (5.5% abv) celebrates the joy of hops. Tropical and citrus aromas plus resinous hops produce an exciting burst of well-balanced flavours.

**UNIT 16B, COQUET
ENTERPRISE PARK, AMBLE
NORTHUMBERLAND, NE65 0PE**
📞 01665 714 855
f @credencebrewing
🐦 @credencebrewing
📷 @credencebrewing

CREDENCE BREWING · NORTHUMBERLAND

CLEAR WATER
NZ HOPPED PALE
4.2%

CREDENCE BREWING · NORTHUMBERLAND

ELEMENTAL IPA
JOY OF HOPS
5.5%

CREDENCE BREWING · NORTHUMBERLAND

WHITE SESSION IPA
MODERN WIT
4.8%

CREDENCE BREWING · NORTHUMBERLAND

RYE IPA
CITRUS AND SPICE
6.8%

CULLERCOATS BREWERY

EST. NOVEMBER 2011
WWW.CULLERCOATSBREWERY.CO.UK

To some it's a British institution, to others it's a lifeline, and to many of us The Shipping Forecast is a range of beers. Cullercoats Brewery has made full use of Cromarty, Forth, Tyne, Dogger etc, to create a series of styles that keep drinkers' satisfaction levels high and brewers' skills levels even higher.

Cullercoats Brewery's core range of beers – Lovely Nelly (3.9% abv), Jack the Devil (4.5% abv), Rocket Brigade IPA (5.5% abv)

and Shuggy Boat Blonde (3.8% abv) – also diversifies into a Fortification selection of ales and a collection called Dry Hop Project. What's more, there are only three of them working on such a busy schedule; Bill and Anna Scantlebury and assistant brewer Sean Hardy.

Cullercoats Brewery, based in Wallsend, Tyne and Wear, was set up after Bill and Anna Scantlebury decided they'd had enough of working for other people. Bill's backyard 50 pint home brewery was transformed into

Bill and Anna Scantlebury with assistant brewer Sean Hardy

Bill Scantlebury

a ten-barrel plant in Wallsend now producing around 5,000 pints a week. They can hear the tumbling North Sea surf and the occasional lifeboat call-out from their home, and it has made them aware of the daily dangers faced by seafarers. So they decided to donate 3p from every pint of Cullercoats Brewery beer to the Royal National Lifeboat Institution (RNLI), the charity that saves lives around the coasts of the British Isles. Donations to November 2017 total £35,000. Cullercoats' first beer, Lovely Nelly, was named in honour of a ship which ran aground off Whitley Sands on New Year's Day in 1861, her crew rescued by Cullercoats lifeboat.

Subsequent beers followed this nautical association, such as the 2014 vintage Royal Sovereign Barley Wine (11% abv) named after Admiral Collingwood's ship at Trafalgar.

Bill Scantlebury has firm ideas about what he wants out of beer and brewing. He's a perfectionist; a nitty-gritty man who likes nothing better than taking part in a hop walk every September to hear the experts talk and to add to his knowledge. He is also fiercely loyal to English hops. For the Dry Hop Project,

They decided to donate 3p from every pint of Cullercoats Brewery beer to the Royal National Lifeboat Institution (RNLI)

Cullercoats insists on dry hopping the old-fashioned way, using a muslin bag of whole leaf hops inside the cask for maximum flavour.

The Shipping Forecast series focuses on the glorious selection of malts available to brewers, while also celebrating the much-loved radio institution. German Bight (4.1% abv) is a Weissbier native to Berlin, Cromarty (4.1% abv) Oatmeal Pale Ale has malt whisky-infused oak chips added to the fermenter, and Dover (4.1% abv) is laced with East Kent Goldings hops.

The Fortified series is in homage to blending strong ale with a weaker one, the way classic Belgian Gueuze is produced. Shuggy Boat Blonde (3.8% abv) with Fortification (7.3% abv) creates Fortified Shuggy (5.0%).

Attention to detail means Cullercoats Brewery has gathered a net full of awards since its first brew. You can just hear the next Shipping Forecast: "General synopsis at 1200 hours. New high expected just west of Tyne."

**UNIT 19, MAURICE ROAD
INDUSTRIAL ESTATE, WALLSEND
TYNE AND WEAR, NE28 6BY**
📞 **07895 692 881**
f @CullercoatsBrewery
🐦 @CullercoatsBrew

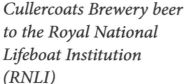

47

D

DARWIN BREWERY

EST. MAY 1997
WWW.DARWINBREWERY.COM

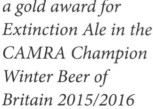

> *The brewery earned a gold award for Extinction Ale in the CAMRA Champion Winter Beer of Britain 2015/2016*

Naming a brewery after a scientist best known for his contribution to the theory of evolution is not such a bad idea. The name Charles Darwin comes with a lot to live up to, but Darwin Brewery in Sunderland has proved well up to the challenge.

The Darwin facility was first set up in 1997 as part of Brewlab, now one of the world's leading providers of training and analysis services for the international brewing industry.

Using a small-scale 100-litre brew plant alongside a 3.5-barrel brewery, Darwin focuses on brewing hand-crafted British ales assisted by students who arrive regularly from the US, South America, South Africa, Greece, Italy, Australia and virtually every point between.

Darwin's equipment is possibly the most eye-catching, highly efficient set of vessels anyone could begin a brewing career on, and it's an obvious source of pride for head brewer Victoria Thomson. Gaining a certificate in brewing competency is one thing, but the real learning starts when making beer on your own equipment. Victoria insists the emphasis is on getting it right, getting it consistent, while also allowing room for experimentation – but the unwavering priority is quality.

Darwin Brewery produces exquisite beers itself, notably Flag Porter (5.0% abv) and Extinction Ale (8.3% abv) with the likes of Galapagos Stout (6.0% abv), Beagle Blonde (4.1% abv) and Rolling Hitch IPA (5.2% abv) in a more than capable supporting role.

Flag Porter was developed from bottles discovered in an 1825 shipwreck in the English Channel. DNA analysis at Brewlab identified the yeast in the sediment which it then cultured and stored, while the malt content was identified as Chevallier, a variety of barley which ceased being used around 1920, but has recently been recreated. Extinction Ale rose from the analysis of bottles dated 1928 and recovered from a house cellar on the North Yorkshire Moors. They had contained strong ale from the Scarborough & Whitby Brewery – a coming of age brew laid down for 21 years.

Flying the flag for the North East, Darwin has won national awards for Rolling Hitch and Hop Drop, while the brewery earned a gold award for Extinction Ale in the Campaign For Real Ale (Camra) Champion Winter Beer of Britain 2015/16.

Some would say Darwin is the natural selection for distinctive drinking. The theory might be right.

UNIT 1, WEST QUAY COURT
SUNDERLAND ENTERPRISE PARK
SUNDERLAND, SR5 2TE
📞 **0191 549 9450**
f **@darwinbreweryltd**
🐦 **@DarwinBrewery**
📷 **@darwinbrewery**

The Dog & Rabbit Brewery EST. JULY 2015

Small business start-ups take their names from all sorts of sources, but not many after a throwaway remark. The Dog & Rabbit microbrewery and micropub in Whitley Bay, Tyne and Wear, earned its name after a guest at owner Tony Patton's 50th birthday party noticed that where he had placed the bar in the garden to serve his home-brewed beer was previously where a rabbit hutch stood.

Tony and his wife Julie had long been thinking about starting their own enterprise and, as they already had a dog, the Dog & Rabbit idea sprouted legs.

The Pattons opened Dog & Rabbit in July 2015 in a former dress shop, and while the micropub got up and running, Tony fitted out some space for a brewery. Friends and family had always praised his home-brew for its commercial quality – and they were right. With the pub running well and attracting praise for its friendly, relaxed atmosphere, Tony has tweaked some of his recipes and now brews twice a week, with all cask and bottle production going through the pub for now.

A chalked sign outside the brewhouse door indicates upcoming brew days; an added attraction for pub customers who love to absorb the malty aromas. Dog & Rabbit beers' reputation has seen collaborations with established breweries Cullercoats (Sea Dog Double Dry Hopped DIPA, 6.0% abv) and Flash House (Hoppy Christmas) with more to follow. In-house beers include Talk To The Paw (5.9% abv), Bad To The Bone (5.0% abv), Whitley Wabbit (5.1% abv), Pavlov's Dog (7.7% abv) and Hare Today Gone Tomorrow (3.7% abv), while yet another animal was the inspiration for Skiffledog Brown Ale (4.6% abv).

Skiffledog is the band now fronted by former Animals lead guitarist Hilton Valentine, who has visited the Dog & Rabbit a couple of times from his home in the US. He played on a string of 1960s classics including House Of The Rising Sun, We Gotta Get Out Of This Place, and Don't Let Me Be Misunderstood.

Tony Patton works on two brewing kits, the bigger one producing 200 litres at a time used for lighter strength beers, and a smaller set with a capacity of 45 litres for stronger ales. A home-brew club now meets there regularly, and members of the Society for the Preservation of Beer in Wood adhere to traditional practices, brewing and maturing their efforts in wooden casks. This is a brewery that will run and run.

**36 PARK VIEW, WHITLEY BAY
TYNE AND WEAR, NE26 2TH**
📞 **07944 552 716**
f **@thedograbbitmicrobrewpub**
🐦 **@thedogandrabbit**

> "
> *Keeping it real;
> real ale, real people,
> real conversation*

Julie Patton

51

THE DURHAM BREWERY

THE DURHAM BREWERY

EST. AUGUST 1994
WWW.DURHAMBREWERY.COM

If ever there was a pioneer in North East brewing, it's the force behind Durham Brewery. Steve and Christine Gibbs set off in 1994 with a mission to combine innovation with tradition. The best part of quarter of a century later, they are still at it, well on top of the game, and ever ready to explore and discover.

Durham Brewery set the pace in light, hoppy beers, influencing drinkers' palates and altering perspectives. The Durham style is to make beers that hold their interest from first sip to final gulp, with a touch of complexity that gives the curious drinker something to mull over. The overriding belief is that brewing is an art form; it has to have subtlety and balance, but it also has to have depth, surprise, and sometimes the ability to shock.

Steve and Christine Gibbs are former music teachers who turned a homebrew hobby into a business when the education system decided that brass (he) and string teachers (she) were no longer required, effectively forcing them to play second fiddle to humanities and

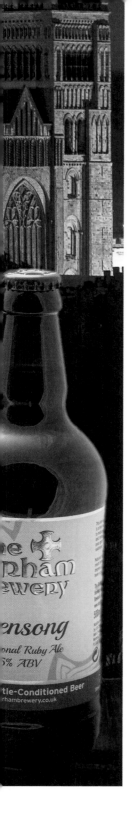

media studies. Durham Brewery operates from an industrial estate in Bowburn, County Durham, but squeezes as many of the city's ecclesiastical connections as possible into naming its beers, such as Evensong, Cloister, St Cuthbert and the best-selling gluten-free Magus. It has consistently grown its portfolio from light bitter to dark stout, wheat beer to Bavarian lagerbier, with an insistence on quality and diversity while cutting no corners and regularly renewing plant and machinery.

Christine's daughter Elly joined the team in 2003 and has been running the day-to-day business for the last few years. Despite its longevity, the family-owned brewery is still small, preferring to concentrate on perfecting beers and processes, ensuring that all styles are made authentically, rather than manufacturing volume.

An astonishing range of beers is brewed on a ten-barrel plant with on-site bottling facilities. Allowing beer to mature properly is almost a Steve Gibbs obsession and cask conditioning means just that - not done in tanks. Keg beer is allowed to mature before kegging and not filtered in order to retain its full flavour. All bottles are bottle-conditioned and never filtered and lagerbier is allowed a full three months to mature naturally. Bottle-conditioned beers have a live yeast sediment

that causes a secondary fermentation and creates a natural sparkle, or fizz, in the bottle.

The results speak volumes – the impressive brewery taproom and shop walls are covered in awards from the likes of the British Bottlers' Institute, the International Beer Challenge, Federation of Small Businesses and countless CAMRA beer festivals, plus World Beer Awards for Diabolus (12% abv) and Finchale Abbaye (10% abv). Brewery tours and open days sell out and markets have opened up worldwide, with the company currently exporting to Australia, Italy, Germany, Switzerland, Austria, France, Belgium and Poland.

Durham is progressing with a sizeable barrel-ageing project using former Scotch whisky casks to mature Imperious (approximately 11.5% abv, as yet to be tested or released) which began life as Temptation Imperial Russian Stout. Diabolus 12% spent 14 months in a whisky hogshead for a limited release of 750 bottles and for autumn/winter 2018 Redemption (approx 11.5% abv) will be released after a lengthy spell in whisky casks.

The Durham portfolio is

> " *Durham has consistently grown its portfolio with an insistence on quality and diversity, cutting no corners and regularly renewing machinery*

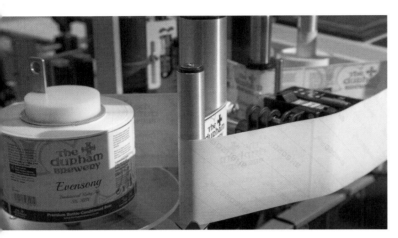

formidable. Magus (3.8% abv) is now always gluten-free, whether cask, bottle, keg or mini cask. Temptation Imperial Russian Stout (10% abv) has coffee and chocolate flavours and an aroma of anise, caramel and blackberries. It's probably Durham's second-best seller, which is surprising given its strength. It gets better with age as it rounds off, fills out and smooths after six months in bottle. Two years is reportedly even better. White Gold (4.0% abv) is next on the popularity list and one of Mitchell & Butlers pub group's Local Hero beers.

Bombay 106 India Pale Ale (7.0% abv) is spicy and peppery with a full-bodied, robust bitterness. Deriving its name from a Durham Light Infantry (DLI) regiment, it's a glorious beer, made with purely English hops and Maris Otter malt. Currently there is a batch maturing in wooden hogsheads as the brewery experiments to create a true 19th Century flavour. Then there is Evensong (5.0% abv) a traditional, well balanced, smooth and malty ruby bitter with hints of kiwi fruit and toffee. Cloister Premium Bitter (4.5% abv) starts with an aroma of grapefruit with notes of

mild pepper and citrus in the flavour. White Stout (7.2% abv), the first pale stout brewed commercially in the UK for 200 years, has perfumy, spicy hop flavours and aromas and a full malt body balanced by forest fruits and mango. It is named after Durham's White range of pale beers and seems to have now become a beer style of its own.

Bede's Chalice Belgian Tripel (9.0% abv) comes with a full fruit body and an aroma of lychees and peaches. St Cuthbert IPA (6.5% abv) has pronounced citrus notes – particularly orange – and a clean peach-like bitterness. Black Bishop Dark Stout (4.1% abv) develops from a rich roast coffee aroma to a clean, smoky finish.

Proving that Durham is never afraid to make changes in the quest to improve a product, the complex Diablous (12.0% abv) returned in 2017 under a new incarnation, emerging from a whisky cask. It was oak aged with a number of yeasts, hints of whisky, sherry and Rioja wine.

There are also high hopes for cask beer Nelson Sauvin IPA (4.7% abv). A single New Zealand hop used at various points during boiling and fermentation brings out its multi-layered fresh and aromatic aspects.

Durham Brewery continues to push and prod while remaining rooted in tradition. Best of all, though, it's still learning - and we're reaping the benefits.

6A BOWBURN NORTH INDUSTRIAL ESTATE, BOWBURN COUNTY DURHAM, DH6 5PF

📞 **0191 377 1991**

❑ **@thedurhambreweryltd**

❑ **@DurhamBrewery**

❑ **@DurhamBrewery**

The new Meheen bottling machine in action, imported from the USA in 2017

FIREBRICK BREWERY BLAYDON-ON-TYNE

FIREBRICK BREWERY LTD

EST. MAY 2012
WWW.FIREBRICKBREWERY.COM

TYNE 9 ABV 3.9% HAND CRAFTED BLACK LAGER
FIREBRICK BREWERY BLAYDON-ON-TYNE

TRADE STAR ABV 4.3% NZ HOPPED AMBER PALE ALE
FIREBRICK BREWERY BLAYDON-ON-TYNE

A spark of revolution illuminates Firebrick Brewery's background. Its first beer, Blaydon Brick, was the nickname of Joseph Cowen, the radical 19th Century politician closely associated with Blaydon's famous brickworks.

Firebrick founder Alistair Lawrence thought it would be entirely appropriate to link his beers to what he calls, "good blokes who made good bricks and improved people's

quality of life". That the brewery stood on Cowen Road in Blaydon, Tyne and Wear, wasn't lost on him, either.

The brewery started in January 2013 and after only one year of operation, expanded, upgrading from a five-barrel brew-kit to a new 15-barrel brewery commissioned from respected manufacturer Malrex, of Burton upon Trent; the spiritual home of beer. The new brewery arrived with varying degrees of hope and trepidation, but also deep-seated confidence. Alistair admits his "go big or go

Michael Brown, brewer, digging out the mash tun

home" decision took him to the point of no return. The brewery now houses five employees.

Firebrick beers, spread extensively throughout the North East, are represented by a Heritage Range inspired by Blaydon's rich history, and a Mystical Range of seasonal beers. The Heritage set is made up of Blaydon Brick (3.8% abv) which has guested at the Strangers' Bar in the House of Commons, plus Stella Spark (4.4% abv), Trade Star (4.2 % abv), Toon Broon (4.6% abv), Elder Statesman (4.5% abv), Coalface (3.9% abv), Tyne 9 (3.9% abv), the mighty Wey-Aye P.A. (5.8% abv) and Giuseppe Lager (4.3% abv).

Firebrick's Mystical Range features illustrations by American artist Wylie Beckert. Pagan Queen (4.0% abv), originally a spring seasonal, emerged to become a permanent fixture, while Heatwave (4.2% abv) and Tormit Heed (4.4% abv) represent summer and autumn respectively, with Fireglow (4.1% abv) ending the year in spicy winter ale style.

Joseph Cowen was at various times a journalist, owner of the Newcastle Daily Chronicle, Member of Parliament, theatre owner and supporter of Irish and Italian revolutionaries. He also campaigned against slavery, for miners' welfare, and equality for women.

In homage, Firebrick has developed gluten-free Giuseppe Lager (4.3% abv), each batch being laboratory tested for its gluten content. Giuseppe Garibaldi, great hero of the Italian Unification movement and revolutionary, stayed with Cowen in 1854 at Stella Hall in Blaydon. Cowen gave Garibaldi a golden sword inscribed, "Presented to General Garibaldi by the People of Tyneside, Friends of European Freedom". Canny Cowen put a penny on the price of The Chronicle to pay for it.

Firebrick is not all about the past, however. The brewery is now kegging beer and there are plans for new 10-barrel bright tanks, a 16-barrel fermenter, in-house bottling or canning, and a shop. In addition, SALSA (Safe And Local Supplier Approval) is underway.

This would complement Firebrick's ARIB qualification (A Revolution In Beer).

> **"**
> *After only one year of operation, Firebrick expanded, upgrading from a loaned five-barrel plant to buying a 15-barrel brewery*

UNITS 10-11 BLAYDON BUSINESS CENTRE, COWEN ROAD BLAYDON-ON-TYNE, NE21 5TW
📞 **0191 447 6543**
📘 **@firebrickbrew**
🐦 **@firebrickbrew**

Alistair Lawrence, head brewer

FLASH HOUSE BREWING CO.

EST. APRIL 2016
WWW.FLASHHOUSEBREWING.CO.UK

Jack O'Keefe and Milda Valutyte caught a bug while travelling in Honduras, Central America. But this was the germ of an idea, not an illness. They had come across a small brewery in a remote part of the country and thought that if beer could be made there it could be made back home in North Shields.

After a year working at Three Kings Brewery in North Shields and a three-week course at the Brewlab training centre in Sunderland, they set up Flash House Brewing Company, a name once used for a Victorian pub full of thieves and women of the night, in April 2016. Jack had also worked in bars around Tyneside, so he knew where the end product is appreciated most. The approach is along the lines of nothing is off-limits, focusing on delivering a wide – and exciting – range of quality beers that include session IPAs, saisons, Cinnabun pale ales, a salt and pepper gose in collaboration with Errant Brewery, Newcastle, and a series of stouts called Shy Bairns Get Stout. Most Flash House production from its five-barrel plant goes into cask, but its can, bottle and keg range has expanded quickly and is expected to develop and grow further. These include Tiny Dancer Pale Ale (5.4% abv),

> *An absolute gorgeous sour blueberry thing, red in colour like a craft drinker has cried blood tears into it...*
> *- Simon E, Untappd*

ENT Session IPA (4.4% abv), Hazelnut Stout (4.7% abv) and Iron Giant IPA (6.0% abv).

The brewery, up the hill from the revitalised North Shields Fish Quay, has also opened an in-house taproom with the aim of opening every weekend in summer 2018. The taproom currently has four cask and four keg lines, and serves an ever-changing line up of Flash House beers to be enjoyed from the source. The bar is constructed from recycled timber and occupies a corner originally earmarked for the extra fermenters the brewery badly needs. When it came to a toss-up, however, elbows on the bar trumped stainless steel.

Milda has been full-time at the brewery since March 2017, and at that time they made a decision not to have a traditional core range of products, going down the experimentation route instead. So now, Flash House will only brew a beer again if they rate it highly enough.

The brewhouse may be limited to 18 casks at a time, but all that means is that Flash House customers can rely on Jack and Milda to continue delivering something new and exciting in the future.

UNIT 1A, NORTHUMBERLAND STREET, NORTH SHIELDS, NE30 1DS
📞 07481 901 875
📘 @flashhousebrewingco
🐦 @flashhousebrew
📷 @FlashHouseBrewing

THE GREAT NORTH EASTERN BREWING CO.

EST. SEPTEMBER 2015
WWW.GNEBCO.COM

Rivet Catcher
CHAMPION BEER OF THE NORTH EAST
SILVER AND BRONZE MEDAL WINNER
AT THE GREAT BRITISH BEER FESTIVAL

ABV 4.0%

I f there was ever a beer that epitomises the North East's formidable industrial heritage, it's Rivet Catcher. It's named after the occupation where shipyard workers would sling red-hot rivets high into scaffolding to be caught in metal buckets then battered into holes in steel plates.

The movements may have been mesmeric, almost graceful, but it was an exhausting and dangerous way to earn a living.

Rivet Catcher is brewed by the Great North Eastern Brewing Company (GNEBC)

in Dunston, Gateshead, and was formerly a Jarrow Brewery stalwart until that company's demise in 2015. Great North Eastern Brewing Co brews out of an impressive facility close to where Federation Brewery once reigned supreme, followed by Scottish & Newcastle between 2005 and 2010.

Today, however, it's Rivet Catcher (4.0% abv), Red Ellen (4.4% abv), Jobling's Swinging Gibbet (4.1% abv), Westoe IPA (4.6% abv), and Clasper's Citra Blonde (3.8% abv) that emerge from the ten-barrel brewhouse. Rivet Catcher

RED ELLEN

JARROW MP AND CRUSADE LEADER 1936
LABOUR REBEL AND REFORMER

ABV 4.4%

THE GREAT NORTH EASTERN BREWING CO. LTD.

email: gneb@mail.com   f Great North Eastern Brewing Company

WOR BOB

ABV 4.8%

THE GREAT NORTH EASTERN BREWING CO. LTD.

email: gneb@mail.com   f Great North Eastern Brewing Company

JOBLINGS SWINGING GIBBET

RECALLING THE MACABRE GIBBETING OF
WILLIAM JOBLING ON JARROW SLAKE

ABV 4.1%

Illustration courtesy of The Paul Perry Collection

THE GREAT NORTH EASTERN BREWING CO. LTD.

email: gneb@mail.com   f Great North Eastern Brewing Company

l-r Managing director Paul Minnikin, head brewer John Stubbs, and trainee brewer Caine Robinson

Matt Aldis, head of distribution

was one of the North East's most popular and award-friendly beers and since its revival has been flying out of the region's pubs, with some casks reportedly lasting little more than two hours.

Other beers in an ever-developing portfolio that celebrates the history of the North East working class include Minnikin's Irish Stout (4.6% abv), Wor Bob (4.8% abv), and Finn's Amber Light (3.6% abv).

William Jobling (Jobling's Swinging Gibbet) was a striking miner famously hanged from a gibbet at Jarrow Slake in 1832, his corpse displayed in a cage, for assaulting a colliery owner. Passing sentence at Durham Assizes, Judge Parke expressed that he had passed the death sentence partly to deter working men from participating in trade unions, and Jobling is still widely considered a North East martyr.

Red Ellen celebrates working class heroine Ellen Wilkinson, a firebrand Labour MP and Minister of Education who came to national prominence playing a pivotal role in the 1936 Jarrow Crusade - the march from Tyneside to London that petitioned for the right to work.

Clasper's Citra Blonde is brewed in honour of Harry Clasper, world champion rower and 19th Century folk hero who built rowing boats to revolutionary designs on the River Tyne at Dunston.

The ten-barrel Great North Eastern Brewing Co brewery is overseen by head brewer John Stubbs. He spent nearly 20 years looking after Vaux Brewery's managed houses and for two years with his partner Carol Graham ran the award-winning Isis pub in Sunderland. It was awarded CAMRA pub of the year for two years in a row, so it's safe to say he knows a thing or two about great beer.

These days, breweries need watertight certification if they want to sell their beer to national customers. It's simply a marker that proves procedures for health and safety and food production are in place, so Great North Eastern Brewing Co is on course for the necessary Safe And Local Supplier Approval (SALSA) accreditation, the food safety certification scheme for the UK's small producers, and a HACCP (Hazard Awareness Critical Control Point) inspection. A SIBA (Society of Independent Brewers) audit has also found everything to be of high specification.

The Great North Eastern Brewing Co project has been largely self-financed, with input from private investors to the tune of £300,000-plus. Phase II is already being worked on with an upgrade to a 30-barrel plant in adjacent

> **Since its revival Rivet Catcher has been flying out of pubs, with some casks reportedly lasting little more than two hours**

buildings with bottling, kegging and canning facilities signed off. A new five-barrel brewery will be used for experimental styles.

From the beginning, managing director Paul Minnikin enlisted the likes of Borders-based Scotia Welding & Fabricating in building and fitting boilers, fermentation vessels and conditioning tanks into the plastic-clad brewhouse alongside a collection of kit and casks sourced from the wider industry. It is a particularly impressive sight.

Scotia Welding stretched veteran Grundy tanks to accommodate double their original capacity of five to ten barrels (16 hectolitres). Grundy tanks – dumpy, domed vessels – were used in pub and club cellars in the 1950s and 1960s to hold large volumes of beer, delivered by tanker then pumped onto the bar counter. They became redundant with the popularity of nine and 18-gallon aluminium casks. Most of them were shipped to the US to be eagerly snapped up by home-brewers. Those same home-brewers were the leaders of the craft beer movement that has been exported back to the UK and these days, Grundy tanks are much sought-after.

An events and live music venue has been created in a unit adjacent to the brewhouse by Mark Forrest and transformed into a seven-days-a-week taproom, snug and shop. The taproom is the ideal way to gauge what the public likes to drink and to trial new beers before they go into full production. It's how Clasper's Citra Blonde was developed into a core product while more experimental brews Dripping Tap and Golden Tap were also assessed.

Visitors could be forgiven for thinking they're relaxing in the residents' lounge of a country hotel, surrounded as they are by soft furnishings, settees, tapestry-backed chairs, frilled lampshades, gilt picture frames and SkyHD served up with 'Geordie tapas'. It's carpeted throughout and candle-lit with a functioning fireplace - perfect for enjoying the brewery's output.

True to working class traditions, Great North Eastern believes in nurturing latent talent and creativity, particularly from those who perhaps haven't had the best start in life. An apprentice brewer is learning the craft well, while another trainee has also responded to having a new direction.

Starting up a brewery of Great North Eastern Brewing Co's size and undoubted potential can't have been easy, but definitely much more fun than battering red-hot rivets into holes.

UNIT E, CONTRACT HOUSE
WELLINGTON ROAD, WEST DUNSTON
GATESHEAD, TYNE AND WEAR
NE11 9HS
📞 **0191 447 4462**
📘 **@GNEBCO**
🐦 **@GNEBCO**
📷 **@GNEBCO**

Head of accounts Carol Graham with Mark Forest, bar tap licensee

16'.0"

![Hadrian Border logo]

HADRIAN BORDER

EST. HADRIAN-1986, BORDER-1992,
HADRIAN BORDER-2000
WWW.HADRIAN-BORDER-BREWERY.CO.UK

STATION EAST

Border Reivers were lawless gangs who engaged in plundering livestock, kidnapping and racketeering in Southern Scotland and North East England. Mercifully, their 21st Century equivalent followed a much more sedate occupation – if brewing beer could ever be classed as sedate.

Hadrian Border Brewery emerged from a fusion of Berwick-based Border Brewery and Newcastle company Hadrian in 2000 and the border raiders Andy and Shona Burrows assumed control of the Byker, Newcastle company. Expansion upon expansion followed and the business grew steadily until it simply could not brew enough beer to meet demand – a frustrating position to be in. Keen to retain a Newcastle address, in 2009 they bought The Preserving Works at Newburn – formerly Ross's pickle factory – on the western fringes of the city. It wasn't a simple case of shifting existing equipment and buying new vessels. The unit was a shell, the roof had to

Owner Andy Burrows with staff member Sam Meagher

be replaced, there was no water, cabling or gas. Walls went up and walls came down and a 40-barrel brewery was installed in 2011, capable of brewing 200 barrels per week.

Business has continued to grow through the popularity of the brewery's wide range of well-balanced beers, by securing supply agreements for major pub companies, while also contract brewing for others who need larger or smaller production runs than they can do themselves.

A 2.5-barrel pilot mash tun, copper and two small fermentation vessels is where small batches and experimental beers first see the light of day. But along with hardware, it's crucial to invest in personnel and quality assurance – being proactive is the key to staying on top. In 2014 the business achieved SALSA (Safe And Local Supplier Approval) and a year later passed the SALSA+beer audit which ensures customers and professional food buyers get the best quality control available.

Brewer Oliver Eltringham was recruited straight from a course at Brewlab training centre in Sunderland to research and develop innovative ideas in the on-site laboratory and ensure quality control and consistency. He is also studying for the Institute of Brewing and Distilling qualifications. Investment has also been put towards researching the export market, with Andy Burrows joining UK Trade & Industry fact-finding trips to Majorca, Denmark, France, India, and more recently China, while an 8.0% abv DIPA has been produced for the Swedish market.

This wasn't the first time a consignment from Hadrian Border had made its way to far-flung regions. When Hexham MP Guy Opperman visited the Falkland Islands with a cross-party group of politicians to strengthen relations with the British overseas territory, he took bottles of Grainger Ale with him.

Hadrian Border has installed 115 solar panels on its roof which could create an output of around 25,000 kW. The project cost over £40,000, but considering the company spends in excess of £15,000 annually on electricity, it was something that needed addressing – along with replacing 100 lightbulbs with LED ones.

Beer is divided into three distinct categories – the Core range, Bandwagon and Specials. The Core range includes best-seller Tyneside Blonde (3.9% abv), a pale thirst quencher; Farne Island (4.0% abv), an amber-coloured traditional bitter; Secret Kingdom (4.3% abv) which is dark, rich and full-bodied; Coast To Coast (4.4% abv), light amber hoppy and malty

> **Business has continued to grow through the popularity of its wide range of well-balanced beers**

Pennine Walker (3.8% abv), brewed for the Pennine Way National Trail where a donation goes with every bottle sold; and a First World War Centenary Ales collection supporting the North East War Memorials Project. Other beers support charities including Daft As A Brush cancer patient transport, Orchid (fighting male cancer), Black and White (NUFC Supporters' Trust) and Trawlerman's Reward for the RNLI.

A natural development and long-term ambition for Hadrian Border was a pub of its own, and when what is now called Station East came up for auction, it stepped in. Located in Gateshead at the end of the Tyne and High Level bridges, the £350,000 project features a quirky space making best use of railway arches and their handsome dressed stonework. This and necessary steelwork incorporated into the design produce an unpretentious industrial feel while creating an atmospheric setting and a convivial place in which to drink.

A brief for a new branding exercise was handed to students at Newcastle College – fresh eyes aren't such a bad thing and a completely radical departure could make all the difference on a busy bar.

Hadrian Border might not subscribe to the warlike attitude of its reiver ancestors, but the brewery retains their spirit and fervour – and has the certificates to prove it.

**UNIT 5, THE PRESERVING WORKS
NEWBURN INDUSTRIAL ESTATE
NEWCASTLE UPON TYNE, NE15 9RT**
📞 **0191 264 9000**
🔲 **@HadrianBorderBrewery**
🐦 **@HadrianBorder**
📷 **@hadrianborderbrewery**

bitter; Northumbrian Gold (4.5% abv) which tastes of biscuit malt with a floral, aromatic aroma; Reiver IPA (4.4% abv), a light golden bitter with a clean citrus palate; gluten-free Grainger Ale (4.6% abv) which uses a single malt and three hop varieties; Tyneside Brown (4.7% abv) which is full-bodied and nutty; and Ouseburn Porter (5.2% abv) - a traditional dark beer brewed using rolled oats for a rich flavour and creamy texture.

The Bandwagon range of beers is more experimental and includes Auld Smokey (4.3% abv), Flaxen (4.1% abv), Rakau (4.2% abv), Lemon Grass (4.4% abv), Star Anise (4.4% abv), Chocolate Cherry Baltic Stout (5.0% abv), American Brown Ale (4.8% abv) and Dunkel (4.4% abv). All are brewed using specialist malts, yeasts, hops and other secret ingredients.

Specials - one-off brews produced to complement the season, the trend, or the mood - are Polska Pale (4.1% abv), an easy-drinker using Polish Lubelski hops; Solar Powered (5.0% abv), the first beer produced using the brewery's new green energy system;

HEXHAMSHIRE BREWERY

EST. 1992
WWW.HEXHAMSHIRE.CO.UK

This makes it Northumberland's oldest brewery – and not many these days would brew their first beers in old dairy tanks

A brewery surrounded by woodland sits at the top end of an attractive beer garden where a mill stream loops round one of the North East's most attractive pubs. Does this sound like beer heaven? Yes, yes, and thrice times yes.

Hexhamshire Brewery, now producing terrific beers in the grounds of the Dipton Mill Inn near Hexham, Northumberland, started life in redundant farm buildings at nearby Ordley in 1992. This makes it Northumberland's oldest brewery – and not many these days would brew their first beers in old dairy tanks.

It also made Geoff Brooker, who began the business with two partners, something of a pioneer, having sensed there was a market for locally brewed beer and that he could supply the Dipton Mill Inn, where he was licensee. Geoff, who passed away in January 2015, was an almost entirely self-taught brewer, shunning fads and fancies to focus on brewing a range of beers to his taste in the expectation that others would enjoy them equally.

His son Mark has continued in this vein, adding his own recipes, including a rye beer, to the brewery's core range whose ingredients are almost all exclusively English with malt from Berwick-upon-Tweed and hops such as Fuggles, East Kent Goldings and Olicana.

During 2017, Mark invested heavily in a new five-barrel electronically controlled brewing kit and highly efficient cask washer which he admits stops him chasing his tail.

Hexhamshire beers range through the dark and moody to bold and fruity, clean and hoppy, and all their names relate to the surrounding countryside. Whapweasel (4.8% abv), named after a local burn, is a dangerously drinkable bitter; Shire Bitter (3.8% abv) is golden and hoppy with biscuit nuances; Devil's Water (4.1% abv) is malty and fruity; Devil's Elbow (3.6% abv) is a soft, creamy auburn ale; and the hoppy pale ale Cragnook Well (4.0% abv) was Hexhamshire's best seller in 2016.

Demand is steadily rising through a number of outlets that include pubs in Newcastle and all over Northumberland, particularly along the Tyne Valley.

The brewery logo is a Thomas Bewick 18th century woodcut which depicts two men in brimmed hats and breeches with a wooden barrel suspended between them. It was some years before it was pointed out that it actually referred to Hexham's leather tanning industry and that they weren't carrying beer, but urine.

**DIPTON MILL ROAD, HEXHAM
NORTHUMBERLAND, NE46 1YA**
📞 01434 606 577
f @hexbrew
🐦 @hexhamshirebrew

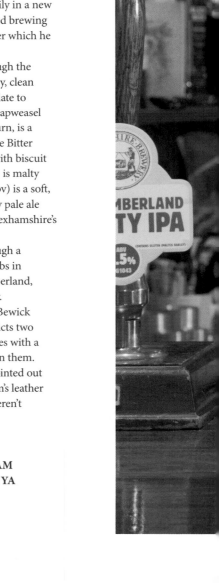

HIGH HOUSE
FARM BREWERY

EST. MARCH 2003
WWW.HIGHHOUSEFARMBREWERY.CO.UK

Repeat after me: "I Ferocious Fred 4.8% abv, take you Lizzie's Dimples 4.0% abv, to be my beer companion, to have and to hold from this day forward..."

Granted, it's not the traditional marriage vow, but it illustrates what High House Farm Brewery does very well – beer and weddings. Hundreds of couples have cottoned on to the benefits of marrying in a brewery and Heather and Gary Scott, owners of High House Farm

Brewery near Matfen in Northumberland, have been delighted by the interest in holding weddings – running at between 70 and 80 a year – in their visitor centre and barns, a collection of Grade II-listed farm buildings designed by John Dobson, the creator of much of Newcastle's glorious Georgian architecture.

High House Farm Brewery sits on a 200-acre working farm, close to the course of Hadrian's Wall. All its beers are named after collie dogs (Auld Hemp, Nel's Best), farm animals (Ferocious Fred, Cyril The

Magnificent), the local surroundings (Matfen Magic, Nettle Ale) and family members (Scotty's Forst, Lizzie's Dimples). As one would expect, heritage and tradition rule the roost with all beers made entirely from all-British malts and English hops. Barley grown on the farm goes off to Thomas Fawcett of Castleford to be malted, but it's impossible to know how much is returned.

The brewhouse occupies handsome barns that remain almost as they were when built, save for the necessary 21st Century cladding and concrete flooring. A large chimney dominates its roofline, a reminder of the steam-driven threshing machine that once hissed and rattled at every harvest.

The ten-barrel brewery with its hot liquor tank, mash tun, copper and five interesting-looking square fermenters brew beer twice a week and often more in line with demand. Lined up in the conditioning room is a row of six Grundy tanks nicknamed Minions, the animated film characters they actually look like in their squat roundness and inspection glass 'eyes'.

High House Farm beers include Auld Hemp (3.8% abv), the first beer the brewery produced, and a fine, amber-coloured

> ## Lined up in the conditioning room is a row of six Grundy tanks nicknamed Minions - characters they actually look like

traditional session bitter with a fresh malty aroma; Nel's Best (4.2% abv) golden premium ale; Matfen Magic (4.8% abv) brown ale with an aroma of hedgerow fruits, malty overtones and a hint of chocolate; Black Moss (4.3% abv), an almost black full-bodied porter with a roasted malt flavour; Sundancer (3.6% abv) seasonal summer light golden ale with overtones of summer berries; and Nettle Beer (4.4% abv) brewed using the nettles that grow prolifically at High House Farm and fresh ginger.

Brewery tours include a potted history of the farm, a detailed explanation of the brewing process, and tutored tastings in the bar, where there's an impressive collection of awards that include being one of eight finalists in the CAMRA Champion Beer of Britain. A three-mile circular walk is also popular from the brewery, passing sites of Roman turrets and milecastles. Tradition, pride and a touch of magic go into every pint of High House Farm beer – a marriage made in heaven.

**HIGH HOUSE FARM, MATFEN
NORTHUMBERLAND, NE20 0RG**
📞 **01661 886 192 or 01661 886 769**
📘 **@highhousefarmbrewery**
🐦 **@highhousebrew**
📷 **@highhousefarmbrewery**

MCCOLL'S BREWERY

MCCOLL'S BREWERY

EST. SEPTEMBER 2016
WWW.MCCOLLSBREWERY.CO.UK

M cColl's Brewery straddles two opposing worlds. Daniel and Gemma's eponymous brewery might be rooted in British beer tradition, but the family business has contemporary plans to create beers across the spectrum.

McColl's Brewery, based in Teesdale, County Durham, produces an initial core range of four beers purposefully showcasing 100% British ingredients. The range includes a traditional Best Bitter (4.4% abv) and an easy going Pale Ale (4.5% abv), alongside a full-bodied IPA (5.0% abv) and a delicate and refreshing Golden Ale (4.0% abv).

Danny, the head brewer, loves to celebrate the country's brewing heritage and sees the classics as the foundation of the brewery before developing an alternative array of beers. For the future, the brewery's plan includes a barrel ageing project, a seriously malt-focused series and a collection of recipes celebrating local produce. Watch this space.

But for now, it is about quality, consistency and building a reputation for the future. So if you want to experience some of the best balanced, perfectly attenuated, flavoursome beers produced in the North East, McColl's should be high on the list.

Danny McColl is someone who needs to get things the way he wants them, and if it takes time – so be it. A home-brewer for ten years, Danny then secured a position at a commercial 20-barrel brewery in the Lake District. Learning the hard way, but giving him the understanding and grounding in good practice, he soon became head brewer.

Then, after completing the advanced brewing course at Brewlab training centre in Sunderland, which he admits opened his eyes to another level of brewing, the McColls began to make plans for their own outfit.

Home to a 20-barrel brewhouse and 40-barrel fermentation capacity, McColl's Brewery started brewing in May 2017. Available in cask and bottle across the North East, McColl's looks to move into keg and can in future, but only when the time is right.

Drawing its inspiration from the likes of Thornbridge, Marble, and Hawkshead, McColl's Brewery is keen to set out its stall as one founded on quality and consistency, where experimentation and constant development is a core tenet of the brewery's philosophy.

> " *Quality, consistency, experimentation and constant development are the core beliefs of our brewery*

UNIT 4 RANDOLPH INDUSTRIAL ESTATE, EVENWOOD BISHOP AUCKLAND COUNTY DURHAM, DL14 9SJ
📞 **01388 417250**
📘 **@mccollsbrewery**
🐦 **@mccollsbrewery**
📷 **@mccollsbrewery**

MORDUE BREWERY

EST. 1995
WWW.MORDUEBREWERY.COM

The Mordue family history started a rewrite in 1995 when two brothers, Garry and Matthew Fawson, were enthusiastic home-brewers tinkering with beer styles for themselves and friends. Then the pair discovered the Wallsend house they were sharing was once part of the 19th Century Joseph Mordue Brewery and, such was the quality of their home-brew, someone mentioned they should go into brewing full-time.

Eager to attain new knowledge through experimentation and building on best practice while brimming with confidence and great intentions, they founded Mordue Brewery and subsequently won Best Beer at the 1995 Campaign For Real Ale (CAMRA) Newcastle Beer Festival with their first commercial brew, Workie Ticket. The phone never stopped.

Two years later, aged 22, Matt Fawson became the youngest brewer to brew a Champion Beer of Britain at the CAMRA Great British Beer Festival, again with Workie Ticket. The phone rang even louder.

Now, 20-odd years later and with a handful of brewery moves, necessary expansions and 60-plus awards to its name, Mordue Brewery is one of the North East's most recognised businesses and Workie Ticket (4.5% abv) is still its best-selling beer by a country mile. The craft beer revolution is one of the most innovative and exciting developments for years in UK brewing. Regardless of being around for more than two decades, Mordue remains at the forefront of the movement.

Brewing standard beers such as Radgie Gadgie (4.8% abv), Five Bridges (3.6% abv) and Northumbrian Blonde (4.0% abv) doesn't mean Mordue has lost its cutting edge - far from it. Seasonal ales and experimental brews underline its capability, its X2 (4.7% abv) dominated by grapefruit and citrus, and Oatmeal Stout (4.5% abv) rounded, smooth and voluptuous.

Meanwhile, the Panda Frog series allows master brewer Rob Millichamp to go off the wall with the likes of the hoppy and sessionable Pandarillo (4.2% abv), Panda Blood IPA (4.9% abv) with blood oranges and citrus hops, and PF Pils (4.7% abv), a Czech-style pilsner.

Mordue is now set to fulfill a long-term ambition by opening its first bar, Beeronomy, in Newcastle, alongside Rhian Cradock, chef proprietor of the Feathers Inn at Hedley-on-the-Hill, Northumberland, who is creating a menu matching food with beer in stylish surroundings.

It might be time to get on the phone.

Matt Fawson became the youngest brewer to brew a Champion Beer of Britain

D1-D2 NARVIK WAY, TYNE TUNNEL TRADING ESTATE, NORTH SHIELDS, TYNE & WEAR, NE29 7XJ
📞 **0191 296 1879**
@mordue.brewery
@MORDUEBREWERY

Robert Millichamp, head brewer

MUCKLE BREWING

EST. APRIL 2016

WWW.MUCKLEBREWING.CO.UK

> "
> *If you can make people smile at a pumpclip you're a long way to selling the beer*

Premier League footballers have 'image rights' inserted into their contracts, Hollywood actors won't get out of bed without them, and even Hadrian's Wall is similarly protected; use of the 1,900-year-old monument for commercial purposes triggering a fee.

Muckle Brewery, based near Haltwhistle in Northumberland, capitalises on the heritage of its near neighbour and happily pays for the privilege. Muckle is north country dialect for something great or big, but it's not a huge brewery; its home is a shed in a garden.

Having said that, when a home-brewing fencing contractor like Tom Smith builds a garden shed, it's not for storing posts, rails and mell hammers. No, he builds a brewery with views across the deep valleys, mature woodland and pine forests of the Tyne Valley, and Muckle Brewery was founded in August 2016 by Tom and his wife Nicola.

The brewery, which features two unusual open-top fermenters, is neat and compact, its 1.3-barrel capacity steaming away twice a week. Tom Smith comes from a well-trodden home-brew tradition, leaning on his dad's old recipe books for knowledge. His first attempt at a lager was a disaster and his brown ale was chewy, but it had all the makings of a decent product, so he stuck at it.

The Smiths have great fun christening beers such as Muckle Chuckle and Muckle Tickle, the theory being that if you can make people smile at a pumpclip you're a long way to selling the beer.

The brewery branding uses images of Crag Lough and the snaking Hadrian's Wall. Muckle Chuckle (4.2% abv) has been crafted with the sound of nearby Haltwhistle Burn bubbling away, while Muckle Buster (4.5% abv), a fruity red ale, connects to the sunsets that highlight the wall's western panorama

Pride of Park (3.5% abv), Muckle's first hazy beer, is light, fruity and inspired by the Northumberland National Park, while Muckle Moss Stout is becoming popular with drinkers who would not normally venture down the dark route. Beers in cask and bottle are delivered in the Smiths' VW campervan to a collection of highly regarded Northumberland pubs, The Sill (Northumberland National Park's visitor centre) and beer specialists in Newcastle, Alnwick and Holy Island, drops often doubling as nights away.

As garden sheds go, the Smiths' may be a fair size, but it's their brewing ambition that's muckle.

3 BELLISTER CLOSE, PARK VILLAGE HALTWHISTLE, NORTHUMBERLAND NE49 0HA

📞 **07711 980 086**
✉ **brewer@mucklebrewing.co.uk**
f **@mucklebrewing**
🐦 **@mucklebrewing**
📷 **@mucklebrewing**

NEWCASTLE BREWING LTD

EST. APRIL 2015
WWW.NEWCASTLEBREWINGLTD.CO.UK

Local produce, local history and a pint at the local – it's a comforting word. And you can't get much more local than a Newcastle microbrewery calling itself Newcastle Brewing then setting up in a former tyre-fitters in the Ouseburn Valley area of the city.

Between them, father and son owners Mike and Leo Bell have more than 70 years of beer drinking experience to call on, so it's fair to say they know what they like. Local is one of them.

For example, a Rhubarb Saison (6.4% abv) they brewed contained 12kg of rhubarb from a Byker garden. Newcastle IPA (5.0% abv) has been described as "the perfect reward for an honest day's work", while Saison Barillas (5.3% abv) is a traditional Belgian farmhouse beer blended with coffees from the neighbouring Ouseburn Coffee Company.

The Bells' introduction to home-brewing came via a Punk IPA kit bought from brewing maverick BrewDog. Inspiration followed and soon they were brewing in Mike's garage, eventually going commercial, but remaining small and local. They founded their first brewery in the Quayside Development Centre in Ouseburn, Newcastle, in 2015.

Fast forward to 2017 and Arch2 Brewpub & Kitchen, a unique venue that has eased itself well into the area's burgeoning artisan and creative atmosphere and the latest move in a trail that has seen brewing equipment grow through 33-litre fermenters, to 55 litres, then 120 litres and on to 200-litres, mastering the craft and learning all the time.

Newcastle Brewing produces more than 20 different flavourful beers including Blondes, Pales, IPAs, Brown Ales, Saisons and Porters, all brewed in rotation.

Arch2 Brewpub & Kitchen, hunkered directly under Byker Bridge, is a community project with local residents, businesses, friends and family raising the funding. The finished article has a light industrial feel, designed by local architects HarperPerry in keeping with the area's manufacturing heritage. Importantly, there is plenty of height in the angled roof for brewery expansion.

The local angle continues with the brewery's branding – striking illustrations by celebrated artist Jim Edwards who has a studio just around the corner. His work straddles cityscapes and abstract images inspired by man-made structures which lend Newcastle Brewing's craft beers a solidity and sense of place.

ARCH2 STEPNEY BANK, OUSEBURN NEWCASTLE UPON TYNE, NE1 2NP

📞 07446 011 941
📘 @NewcastleBrewing
🐦 @nwcstlbrewing
📷 @newcastlebrewing

> *Mike and Leo Bell have more than 70 years of beer drinking experience, so they know what they like*

RIGG & FURROW

EST. FEBRUARY 2017
WWW.RIGGANDFURROW.COM

Rigg and Furrow may only have been founded in the early part of 2017, but a mere four brews later there were more than 40 pubs on the delivery sheet around Northumberland and into some prime spots in Newcastle.

The name has not emerged from a brainstorming branding exercise, but is site-specific and loaded with personal references.

A rigg and furrow is a wave-like pattern of ridges and troughs formed by aeons of ploughing. The phenomenon is clearly visible on the farm's pastureland bordered by the River Coquet – and it's where brewery owners Theo and Pippa were married.

Returning from honeymoon to Acklington Park, where the Howies have farmed since 1962, they put their long-incubating brewery ideas into practice.

Rigg & Furrow operates on two floors of a former milking parlour – the ten-barrel brewhouse is fed from the malt store upstairs in much the same way as the dairy cattle were before the bottom fell out of that particular market. Next door are fermentation and cold rooms and beyond those sits an area ripe for a brewery tap.

Bottling and mini-kegs are the next step so fortunately plenty of expansion room comes with buildings on 350-acre farms.

Rigg & Furrow pumpclips feature farm animals – Aggie the Highland cow stars on The Pale Ale (3.8% abv), while the resident Indian Runner ducks are illustrated on Run Hop Run (4.2% abv).

Plans include growing Golden Promise barley – the variety much prized in the Scotch whisky industry and malted at Simpson's in Berwick. Spent grains are fed to the farm's beef cattle and their manure spread on the fields as fertiliser.

Experimenting with farm grown wheat and oats is also an option, as is using native wild yeast strains to craft beers that will reflect their surroundings and have a sense of place, or terroir.

Rigg & Furrow's core beers are The Pale Ale (3.8% abv English Pale), Run Hop Run (4.2% abv Simcoe Single Hop), Owl Porter (4.0% abv), and Trickster (4.3% abv hoppy Amber Ale) supplemented by seasonal farmhouse ales brewed with ingredients from the farm. Recent brews have included Rhuble brewed with rhubarb, Sham Pain brewed with elderflower, and Bramble brewed with blackberries.

All going well, the troughs at Rigg & Furrow should be few and far between.

ACKLINGTON PARK FARM
NORTHUMBERLAND, NE65 9AA
 @riggandfurrow
 @riggandfurrow
 @riggandfurrow

> " *A rigg and furrow is a wave-like pattern of ridges and troughs formed by aeons of ploughing*

ROUNDHILL BREWERY

EST. FEBRUARY 2017
WWW.ROUNDHILLBREWERY.CO.UK

Cleaning small, enclosed vessels is an inescapable situation in a brewery. So, consider that Roundhill Brewery owner Russell Allen – a fairly tall chap – is at a real disadvantage, suffering as he does from claustrophobia.

He couldn't sleep the night before his first commercial brew in February 2017, but the cure-all of a simple dangling inspection lamp swept those fears aside and a new career was up and running.

Russell Allen had been home-brewing for 40 years which honed and fine-tuned his recipe skills. He subsequently took a course at Brewlab training centre in Sunderland, which confirmed that what he had been doing all these years was right.

He started Roundhill Brewery after leaving his job in software, but curiously the five-barrel brewery is controlled by hand and eye with not a computer in sight. He refers to his hand-crafted methods as "proper brewing, not push-button" and instead of labels stuck on the bottles, he strings tags around their necks. Having said that, he's adamant he's not against technology – only technology for technology's sake.

Russell believes beer should be a living product presented to the consumer in unfiltered and unpasteurised form which retains the flavours and aromas he strives for in the likes of Roundhill Brown Ale (4.9% abv); the subtly fruity Dark Ale (5.2% abv); copper-coloured Bitter (4.1% abv); Billingham Pale Ale (5.2% abv) which is hoppy and zesty, Midnight Slug Porter (4.8% abv); and Pale & Golden (4.2% abv). This approach could arguably lead to slight variations between batches, which he's perfectly happy with, although regular Roundhill drinkers praise the beers' consistency.

Russell's beers are on pub counters in Redcar, Stockton, Darlington, Hartlepool, Seaton Carew and Middlesbrough with successful forays into CAMRA beer festivals raising awareness further. Roundhill Brewery is a real family enterprise with Russell's wife Angela helping out, particularly on bottling days, and he reckons he lost a great brewer when youngest daughter Sophie went off to university. It's noticeable there are no chairs in the compact, light and airy industrial unit. Resting awhile means pulling up a sack of malted barley, which is surprisingly comfortable, as it happens. There's never any time to sit down anyway, is the Allen argument. Plans in the pipeline include individual and group brew days and weekend brewery visits – Daddy Daycare, he calls it.

> " Beer should be a living product in unfiltered and unpasteurised form

UNIT 1, LAGONDA COURT
BILLINGHAM, STOCKTON-ON-TEES
TS23 4JF
📞 07910 567 847
f @roundhillbrewery
🐦 @roundhillbrew
📷 @roundhillbrewery

Sonnet 43

BREW HOUSE

SONNET 43 BREW HOUSE

EST. SEPTEMBER 2012
WWW.SONNET43.COM

Elizabeth Barrett Browning is better known for her poetry than for raising a glass of beer to her lips. Yet the Victorian poet is the inspiration behind one of the North East's most progressive craft breweries.

Sonnet 43 Brew House, based in a former MoT testing station in Coxhoe, County Durham, was named after one of Barratt Browning's most illustrious verses – also known as How Do I Love Thee? – and

because she was born at nearby Coxhoe Hall in 1806.

Following a £200,000 investment and securing the services of experienced brewer Michael Harker, Sonnet 43 Brew House brewed its first beer in October 2012 and quickly established itself in the North East beer psyche through product quality and a thorough understanding of raw materials and how varieties of hops and malted barley can be exploited in the search for balance and drinkability. There are also four

Brewery manager Alan Brown and Michael Harker, head brewer

pubs under the Sonnet 43 branding, plus a hotel, several restaurants, including The Italian Farmhouse restaurant next door to the brewery, and a gin distillery, all part of Tavistock Hospitality group.

Its managing director Mark Hird trained as a chef and completed a course at Brewlab in Sunderland to understand the brewing process. His instinctive feel for what people want to eat and drink is backed by the science and microbiology he learned at Brewlab, plus the knowledge of how to shovel malt and appreciate the smell of fresh hops.

Sonnet 43 Brew House is described as, "the classic tight fit", and it's quite remarkable how many brewing vessels can be fitted into a compact unit. But by extending fermenters upwards and with a shuffle here and there, the arrangement works beautifully. Hoses coil around brew kettles, a filtration unit looks seriously efficient, and glorious malty aromas rise from fermenters every time a lid is raised.

There are five brew days a week, often more when demand rises, and thoughts are on an area at the back of the brewery to expand volumes which could virtually treble output.

Now more than five years in – and with many new breweries and a great deal of change on the pub and bar scene to contend with, Sonnet 43 continues to learn and grow with beer trends and customer demands in order to keep brewing what discerning drinkers will enjoy.

The aim is to sustain the quest to produce the quality cask ales the brewery has become known for whilst offering small pack options further into the licensed trade including regional supermarkets, and to continue to indulge its brewers' creativity with new and exciting releases.

Sonnet 43 expects to expand in this sector and has plans to develop its bottle and can offering to be able to distribute these more widely beyond its direct delivery routes which cover most of North East England and South East Scotland.

Its brewers are also keen to play with their new piece of kit – a hop rocket – and use it to create new additions to the Rogue range and one-off experimental beers as well as making slight adjustments to some of the existing ales for a little extra hop kick.

Three distinct categories form the Sonnet 43 portfolio; the Core range of

> *Experimentation and innovation have been rewarded with 59 awards in five years*

in little over five years from the Campaign For Real Ale (CAMRA), SIBA - the Society of Independent Brewers - and the Guild of Fine Food; organisations that know their aromatics from their esters.

It goes without saying that Sonnet 43 takes an ultra-modern look at its brand identity. From early on, the brewery commissioned a bold, typographical style, but striking visuals have evolved more recently, while not ditching the letterforms completely.

Some of the imagery – Raven Bourbon Milk Stout and Abolition Amber Ale, for example – are works of art in themselves, while Yellow Cab Lager and Fierce Panther are graphically direct, bright, to the point and hit you in the eye, which doesn't go unnoticed on a busy pub counter.

Mark Hird fully understands that a strong look is invaluable for a brewery to ensure its beers catch the eye on a bar, so it's important to get it right; after all, it can also be a good indicator of quality.

Quality and innovation are at the heart of Sonnet 43 Brew House with everything being done "for the love of beer".

Using this ethos as their guide, they aim to continue brewing their sessionable core ales as well as creating new, big-hitting beers all with their signature striking look.

How do I drink to thee? Let me count the ways.

crowd pleasers, a Rogue range, and an Experimental range. Rogue beers (available in keg and can) such as Fierce Panther Pale Ale (6.9% abv), Miss Scarlet's Revolver (6.8% abv), a toasted coconut mocha porter, and Yellow Cab Lager (4.1% abv) have allowed the brewery to drive along the US-influenced hop character road, while the experimental #34 People We Trust (4.5% abv), a Kentucky common ale, and #41 The Right Brew, a 5.6% abv blood orange Munich wheat beer, have been particularly well received with a discerning customer base that has expanded far beyond the North East.

The Core range features, among others, Athenaeum Extra Pale Ale (4.8% abv), The Raven Bourbon Milk Stout (4.3% abv) and Impressment American Pale Ale (5.6% abv) which uses six varieties of US hops for its intense tropical and citrus notes. All their names are inspired by the life and works of Elizabeth Barrett Browning.

Experimentation and innovation like this have been rewarded with 59 awards

DURHAM ROAD, COXHOE
COUNTY DURHAM, DH6 4HX
📞 **0191 377 3039**
📘 **@sonnet43**
🐦 **@sonnet43brew**
📷 **@sonnet43brewhouse**

Michael Harker, head brewer

STU BREW

EST. AUGUST 2013
WWW.STUBREW.COM

> ## Stu Brew is a social enterprise; students develop recipes, brew the beer and sell it, overseen by project coordinators

Stu Brew is the first student-run brewery in Europe. Based at Newcastle University, its ales are served in campus bars as well as in local pubs, restaurants and bottle shops. Stu Brew's flagship beer, Textbook IPA (4.5% ABV) is a punchy pale brewed with Mosaic hops, whilst Red Brick (4.8% abv) is a full-flavoured amber defined by its complex malt character and has been described as a perfect after-work beer. Lab Session (4.3% abv) provides a lighter option, with a paler malt bill and masses of Chinook and Simcoe giving a refreshingly crisp finish.

Stu Brew is a social enterprise run as a society within Newcastle University Students' Union; students develop, brew and sell the beer, overseen by project coordinators who ensure their studies run smoothly alongside their brewery adventures.

Members aren't just limited to brewing - management, marketing, creative design, distillations and events are all managed by students.

In return for their time, Stu Brew members gain valuable work experience and a unique opportunity to develop new skills. All profits are reinvested into training, ensuring long-term sustainability. A number of students have gained jobs in the brewing industry with the likes of Heineken, BrewDog, Camerons and various local micro-breweries.

Stu Brew's other major focus is sustainability; combining a passion for great beer with environmental responsibility. Researchers in the School of Engineering, led by Dr Chris O'Malley, focus on a number of studies. These range from waste disposal, to sustainable resource use, particularly the best use of spent grains, hops and yeast, plus anaerobic digestion and gasification. These findings are then made available to other local breweries to share best practice.

The brewery staff – the students – closely monitor energy and water usage to increase efficiency when heating and cooling. Spent grains are not thrown away, but used as animal feed, and waste hops serve as mulch for Go Volunteer's orchard; so even after the brew is complete, the savings for the environment are considered. Newcastle University's Cockle Park Farm provides a further opportunity, where a dedicated volunteer team have been growing their own hops, with harvests of Cascade and Chinook brought in for the first time in 2017.

NEWCASTLE UNIVERSITY STUDENTS' UNION, KINGS WALK NEWCASTLE UPON TYNE, NE1 8QB
📞 **0191 239 3900**
f **@stubrewncl**
🐦 **@stubrewncl**
📷 **@stubrewncl**

Three Kings Brewery

THREE KINGS BREWERY

EST. APRIL 2012
WWW.THREEKINGSBREWERY.CO.UK

Three Kings Brewery owner Ewan McCann has a weakness. Hops. He is often asked his favourite variety and will willingly rattle off "Nelson Sauvin, Cascade, Citra, Comet, Simcoe, Mosaic, Centennial…" before admitting that it's a question that's impossible to answer. What he does know, however, is that he spends "a fortune" on the little green leaves.

Another weakness – or passion – is cask and bottle-conditioned beers: th___ what he likes

to drink, so that's the vast bulk of the North Shields brewery's output, although with an eye on the ever-changing marketplace it is now producing more keg beer.

Three Kings is named in honour of the kings buried within the walls of Tynemouth Priory – Oswin, Osred and Malcolm – and represented as crowns on the Borough of Tynemouth's coat of arms. The lion rampant prominent on the Three Kings branding refers to Malcolm, the sole Scot among the Northumbrian trio.

Three Kings beers use nothing more than

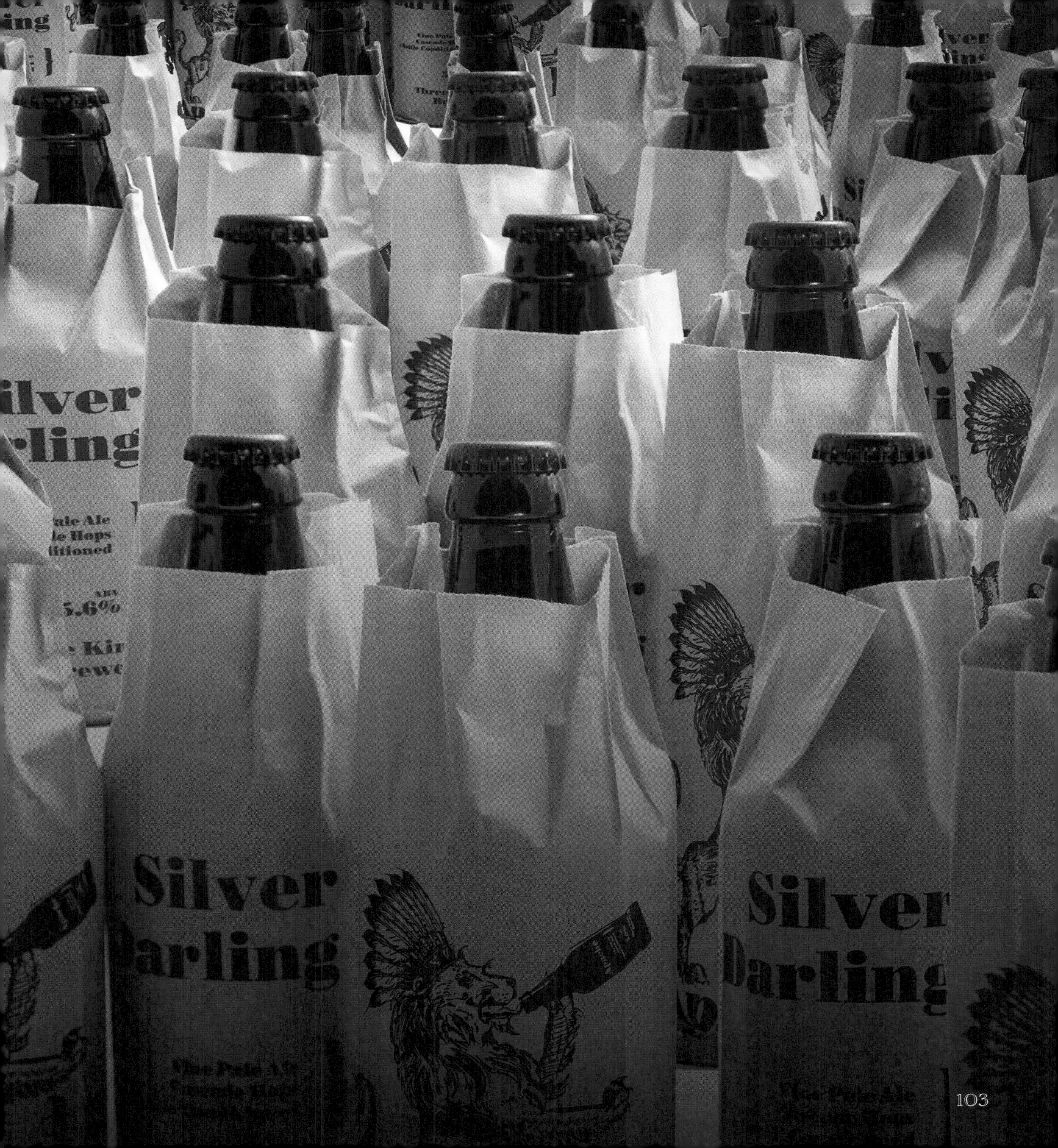
Silver
ABV

malted barley, hops, yeast and water to create outstanding aromas, flavours and mouthfeels. They are well made with no frills, employing premium ingredients to produce the likes of Billy Mill Golden Bitter (4.0% abv), Ring of Fire American Pale Ale (4.5%), Shieldsman Bitter Blonde Ale (3.8% abv), Silver Darling Pale Ale (5.6% abv) and Dark Side of The Toon Irish Stout (4.1% abv). All names have North East connotations with particular reference to North Shields. Three Kings undertook a massive expansion in December 2015, elbowing into the next-door unit and spreading its new ten-barrel brew kit into the freedom of the new space – marking a progression through its 2.5-barrel start-up, then onto five barrels. Brewing takes place two and three times a week, depending on the cycle of orders and the season.

Deliveries go out to 100 pubs throughout the North East. Two new beers are produced a month which keeps interest fresh, while pub house beers can be found at the Oddfellows and the Low Lights Tavern in North Shields, The Rockcliffe Arms, Whitley Bay, plus the Telegraph and the Newcastle Arms in Newcastle.

Three Kings' bottled beers are distinguished by their brown paper wrap-arounds rather than normal labels, a unique selling proposition that works well for Apache American Pale (5.0% abv), Silver Darling Pale Ale (5.6% abv) and Tyneside Tommy Best Bitter (4.1% abv).

Tyneside Tommy was produced by Three Kings for the Tynemouth World War One Commemoration Project. The beer, produced from 2014 until November 11, 2018 has spread awareness of the Great War, its aim to raise money to place blue plaques on the former homes of soldiers from Tynemouth, North Shields and Whitley Bay who fell in the 1914-18 conflict. Again, the labelling for the centenary project took a different approach, cleverly using looped, loose-label dog tags.

Ewan McCann is also a pioneer in traditionally maturing beer in wood. Sitting quietly in the brewery's cold store are 125-litre whisky casks of beer used for the past 50 years, first for maturing bourbon and then single malt whisky. In some card games, the player who is dealt three kings wins. Snap.

**14/15 PROSPECT TERRACE
NORTH SHIELDS
TYNE AND WEAR, NE30 1DX**
📞 **07580 004 565**
f **@threekingsbrewery**
🐦 **@threekingsbeer**

> " *Beers are traditionally produced, using nothing more than malted barley, hops, yeast and water to create outstanding aromas, flavours and mouthfeels*

Ewan McCann, owner and brewer

TWICE BREWED
BREW HOUSE
HADRIANS WALL

TWICE BREWED
BREW HOUSE

EST. JULY 2017
WWW.TWICEBREWEDBREWHOUSE.CO.UK

I t's six o'clock in the morning. The sun has wakened the vast bulk of Steel Rigg, picking out the ribbon of Hadrian's Wall on the ridge. It's glorious, inspirational and emotive.

It's also the view that greets Twice Brewed Brew House head brewer Red Kellie at the start of her shift in the spacious five-barrel facility on the B6318 Military Road near Bardon Mill in Northumberland.

Twice Brewed Brew House, attached to the Twice Brewed Inn, is a purpose-built, highly impressive, stone-built space, completed in June 2017 with its first beer rolling out a month later.

Red Kellie was involved with Twice Brewed before a dressed stone was laid, advising on building plans, layout, configuration of brewing vessels and a taproom with a fully fitted bar available for wedding receptions, meetings, training and brewery visits.

She has free rein to develop styles, play around and brew beer that customers will seek out, at first in the hugely popular

pub next door, plus the Red Lion at Newbrough and the Hadrian Hotel at Wall, both in Northumberland and under the same ownership.

Red is constantly mindful that the market in this part of Northumberland leans heavily towards the traditional and is quite different from large town and city centre tastes. She was also involved in the start-up and running of Stu Brew at Newcastle University, Europe's first student microbrewery, and also founded First And Last, her own brewery in Elsdon, Northumberland.

It's handy that assistant brewer Matthew Brown is also responsible for ordering beer for the pub, so he knows what customers want, which informs what's brewed.

Twice Brewed beers include Best Bitter (3.8% abv), Ale Caesar American Amber (4.3% abv), Sycamore Gap Pale Ale (4.1% abv) and Vindolanda Excavation IPA (5.3% abv). It's a sensible core range, given that enthusiasts tackling Hadrian's Wall, the Pennine Way and Hadrian's Cycleway will prefer thirst-quenchers at the end of a challenging day. They're a community of wallers from all nations on a shared journey to neighbouring sites including the Roman forts of Housesteads, Vindolanda and the Roman Army Museum, and The Sill National Landscape Discovery Centre.

Dry-hopping beers, wheat beers, red rye, stouts and porters are on the to-do list now that the core range is heading out across the North East, North Yorkshire and Cumbria. Every Twice Brewed beer has a story to tell, either through local history or points on the landscape. Archaeologists on the dig at Vindolanda will come in and drink 'their' beer and often be coaxed into helping on a brew.

The origins of the Twice Brewed name range from beer having to be brewed again – and stronger – to fortify soldiers before the Battle of Hexham in 1464, to Lady Hexham doing much the same with tea in her drawing room. But the more likely source is the two brows - 'brews' - of hills where drovers' roads converge.

Twice Brewed's vision and energy are influenced by its unique setting. Hadrian's Wall is a vibrant, multicultural monument. Frontier spirit, it's called.

> "
> *Archaeologists on the dig at Vindolanda will come in and drink 'their' beer and often help on a brew*

TWICE BREWED INN, BARDON MILL NORTHUMBERLAND, NE47 7AN
📞 **01434 344 534**
f **@twicebrewedinn**
🐦 **@twicebrewedinn**

Andy Smith, general manager, and Red Kellie, head brewer

Two By Two Brewing EST. SEPTEMBER 2014

The nursery rhyme tells us the animals came in two by two. Two by two is a versatile piece of timber used in building projects – and more significantly, Two By Two is also one of the North East's most innovative microbreweries.

Two By Two Brewing brewed its first beer in 2014 and owner Rob MacLeod reckons they're now so popular, he'll need to expand out of his unit in Wallsend, Tyne and Wear, so there's a distinct possibility that the wood analogy will come in handy. Putting in a mezzanine floor to allow for brewhouse expansion was considered, but an empty space where an upgraded brewery can be planned properly is too great a temptation.

Pubs supplied include The Cluny's house beer, the Tyne Bar, Cumberland Arms and Free Trade in the Ouseburn Valley. Deliveries to Edinburgh and Leeds once a month take beer further afield and though Two By Two beers proved popular on a foray into London, Rob reckons he's too busy with the local market to do that regularly.

In his earlier career, Rob McLeod worked at The Bridge Hotel in Newcastle where he developed a keen interest in beer styles, then in other pubs where his enthusiasm developed further. He enrolled on the intensive Diploma in British Brewing Technology course at Brewlab in Sunderland, where students not only learn the theory of brewing but also the practical side, microbiology and business start-up.

Two By Two brew beers include Bergamot Citra Saison (5.2% abv), Chinook Pale (5.0% abv), Sitting Duck Stout (5.7% abv), Southpaw (6.2% abv) and Ugly Duckling (4.8% abv), a beer brewed using bread from the Ugly Duckling company, which promotes the use of surplus foods. More of this is following with plans to collaborate on a range of sours. He has brewed an IPA in support of Ouseburn Farm, the charity that brings awareness of rural life and animal welfare into the city, particularly for schoolchildren and people with varying degrees of learning difficulties and disabilities. One quarter of the profits from the beer is donated to help keep it viable following local authority cuts in funding.

Running at full tilt to keep up with demand means beers can only be brewed one by one. Come the new premises, though, Two By Two would be rather appropriate.

> " *Moving closer to Newcastle, where most of the Two By Two range is sold, would be an advantage*

UNIT 19 POINT PLEASANT INDUSTRIAL ESTATE, WALLSEND TYNE AND WEAR, NE28 6HA
📞 07723 959 168
f @Twobytwobrewing
🐦 @Twobytwobrewing
📷 @Twobytwobrewing

Rob Macleod, owner and brewer

TYNE BANK BREWERY

EST. 2011
TYNEBANKBREWERY.CO.UK

Right from its beginnings in 2011, Tyne Bank Brewery managed one of the best beer business start-up tricks in the book. It attracted the affection and admiration of North East beer lovers and, crucially, rival brewers.

Perhaps the timing was right, or the fact that owner Julia Austin had quickly established herself as a genuine player – or perhaps it was because head brewer Adam Brewer had the perfect beer name.

All of those came into the equation, but brewing well-balanced beers with flavour and adventure in every sip certainly helped Tyne Bank assert itself in the region's beer conscience.

Now ensconced in a red brick building on Newcastle's Walker Road, Tyne Bank has developed its original 20-barrel brewhouse alongside an events space with an attached taproom and bar that regularly attracts artisan markets, live music and DJs.

A crest on the front of the building displays a royal warrant of appointment, so the brewery already had a lot to live up to. Additionally, roughly where the car park is now was once the home of Newcastle East End Football Club, which amalgamated with Newcastle West End FC in 1892 to form Newcastle United.

The brave move into these premises was accelerated by a crowdfunding initiative; an opportunity for a community of like-minded people to pool their money and knowledge to back start-up businesses, in Tyne Bank's case giving supporters the opportunity to become 'armchair Dragons'. Also part of the bigger picture is that visitors can watch how the beer is made, drink it, and enjoy the whole experience. The mantra goes, "it's what we put into it that guarantees what you get out of it".

Tyne Bank brews a formidable set of core beers; Silver Dollar American IPA (4.9% abv), Monument Bitter (4.1% abv), Northern Porter (4.5% abv) and West Coast IPA (4.0% abv) can be spotted in the North East's most discerning pubs and are also available in bottle and can.

They are supplemented by a formidable range that includes Strawberries & Cream (3.8% abv), Rhubarb & Custard (4.4% abv), Motueka Blonde (4.0% abv), Mocha Milk Stout (6.0% abv), Cherry Stout (5.0% abv) and the highly sessionable Summer Breeze (3.9% abv) distinguished by the use of lemongrass and root ginger.

That's right, it's what you put into it...

> *It's what we put into it that guarantees what you get out of it*

375 WALKER ROAD
NEWCASTLE UPON TYNE, NE26 2AB
📞 **0191 265 2828**
f @TyneBankBrewery
𝕐 @TyneBankBrewery
◻ @tynebankbrewery

VIP Brewery Alnwick

VIP BREWERY ALNWICK

EST. JULY 2012
WWW.VIPBREWERY.CO.UK

Stepping into the VIP brewhouse is like stumbling across an old barn somewhere remote and discovering a forgotten classic Daimler. It takes you by surprise.

Hawkhill Business Park in Lesbury, Northumberland, is not exactly remote, but you're greeted inside its huge barn door by a collection of lovely honey-brown, timber-clad brewing vessels – one sitting above another to start off the brewing process by gravity, just like the Victorians did for us.

Three fermenters and two conditioning tanks help fill the room, all of which says more about small spaces than a devotion to historic brewing methods. The fact that the former farm buildings with their high-pitched ceilings were previously used for raising turkeys adds another layer of mystery and imagination.

VIP was established in 2012 by Phil Bell and two friends. However, in 2016, The Alnwick Brewery Company bought into the business to help it produce some of its own beer brands alongside VIP's popular beers that include The Village Bike (4.0% abv), The Village Copper (4.2% abv), and The Village Ghost (4.5% abv).

Phil Bell remains from the original trio and is not only head brewer, having studied at Brewlab training centre in Sunderland, but puts his hand to welding, plumbing and steel fabricating. Microbrewers tend to be a versatile breed.

He also fell in love with the brewery's home as soon as he walked through its gates after looking at various industrial units in the area. Being less than a mile from the coast at Alnmouth wasn't lost on him either, with visitor centre opportunities tied in with sister companies Alnwick Rum and Lindisfarne Mead.

The five-barrel brewery works flat out four and five days a week, supplying outlets principally around Northumberland.

VIP's courtyard, a suntrap sheltered by high stone walls, is perfect for hosting beer festivals and music events and this will be capitalised upon with an imminent expansion into an extensive area next door – although the brewing vessels will move in, tucked under a grain store, they are expected to retain their current production volume.

VIP is in a very important position – on top and moving nicely.

> **VIP's courtyard, a suntrap sheltered by high stone walls, is perfect for hosting beer festivals and music events**

UNIT E-F, HAWKSHILL INDUSTRIAL ESTATE, LESBURY, ALNWICK NORTHUMBERLAND, NE66 3PG
📞 01665 830 617
f @VIPbrewery
🐦 @VIPBrewery1
📷 @VIPBrewery1

Phil Bell, owner and brewer

WHITLEY BAY BREWING CO. EST. APRIL 2016

Visitors to Whitley Bay can expect to come across a new species of seagull, and it's flying out of the town's first microbrewery.

Seagull Pale Ale (4.2% abv) was commissioned from Whitley Bay Brewing Company by celebrated author Ann Cleeves, creator of the Vera Stanhope detective novels that have also proved extremely popular in their ITV adaptation, Vera. The Seagull is the name of the eighth book in the series, set in Whitley Bay.

Whitley Bay Brewing started in April 2016 in a storage space and former kitchen premises to the rear of the King George pub close to the seafront in the town. Brewing ales for the bar seemed like a natural progression after two years of pulling pints and a five-barrel plant was eventually installed, complete with viewing window from the bar.

Its first brew was Spanish City Blonde (4.2% abv) named in honour of the famous domed visitor attraction, followed by Warrior (3.9% abv) in celebration of Whitley Warriors ice hockey team. A donation of 10p from every pint is generously given to the players' fund.

Several house ales for local pubs have been brewed, along with Ghost Ships (4.3% abv), a beer that commemorated five huge vessels anchored and seemingly abandoned off Whitley Bay because their owners had gone out of business. But hardly had the beer hit the counter than they had slipped their moorings and disappeared into the night.

Brewery owners Gavin Hattrick and Gary Harding had never brewed before, but Ewan McCann from Three Kings Brewery in North Shields helped to develop recipes and source equipment. He is happily on hand to help latest brewery recruit Jaimie Cooper, who only asked if she could help with the IT side, but has picked brewing up particularly well, to the extent that she says it has changed her life.

Two fermentation tanks, mash tun and a hot liquor tank came from Fort William-based Oban Ales, a brewing equipment manufacturer with quite a presence in the North East. Around two brews every ten days are produced with a 55° North Pilsner (5.5% abv) next on the roster, pinpointing Whitley Bay's geographical location.

One by-product of the brewery is King George customers getting more involved in beer culture, building a community of ale-lovers. Vera, however, is yet to investigate.

> Its first brew was Spanish City Blonde, named in honour of the famous attraction...

1-2 EAST PARADE, WHITLEY BAY
NEWCASTLE UPON TYNE
TYNE AND WEAR, NE26 1AW
📞 07392 823 480
f @WhitleyBayBrewingCompany

117

WYL

WYLAM BREWERY

EST. SEPTEMBER 2000
WWW.WYLAMBREWERY.CO.UK

Wylam Brewery owes its origins to a postcard in a newsagent's window. It was set up in 2000 in a Northumberland farm milking parlour shortly after John Boyle and the late Robin Leighton put their heads together over an unresponsive computer. John came to Robin's rescue, and while fixing the huffy computer, discovered they shared an interest in home-brewing and that perhaps they should

collaborate. Wylam Brewery today occupies one of Newcastle's most iconic buildings, The Palace of Arts in Exhibition Park, where it has developed a brewing centre of excellence. The building was originally built in 1928 for the North East Coast Exhibition and it is the only structure left from that attempt to revitalise the city and the region after the Great Depression. Creating a brewery, taproom and kitchen, brewing education facility, multi-use events space and visitor centre in a £2.2m investment was a highly attractive proposition, particularly

for a city that encourages vibrant enterprises. Still in its original but much expanded farm premises in 2012, an investment by Greenan Blueaye (named in deference to David Bowie) allowed Wylam Brewery to acquire new equipment, increase output and shift up a gear with fresh ideas and freed-up beer styles. Greenan Blueaye directors Rob Cameron and Dave Stone genuinely loved the Wylam products and their confident approach brought a new impetus into making beer and exploring new markets.

They also fell in love with the Palace of Arts as soon as they walked into the domed lakeside building. It was an empty space where owner Shepherd Offshore had proposed to store a collection of veteran vehicles, but the thought of bringing it back into public use was too exciting a prospect to ignore.

They also saw the potential of creating a brewery tap and visitor centre, both hugely important elements in brewing these days. Wylam set on a mission to study other brewing operations which shared its vision at home and across the US, and staff members needed no encouragement to contribute their ideas.

A similar 30-barrel capacity brewery to Beavertown Brewery's in London was commissioned following several brewing collaborations. Beavertown's ex head brewer Jenn Merrick had been graced with a brewer of the year award and highly recommended the impressive collection of vessels.

A lot has happened in the world of brewing since 2000; palates and minds have opened with drinkers venturing more into styles and flavours once the preserve of European brewers which were shipped across the Atlantic to be tweaked, supercharged or reinvented only to be brought back to take the adventure even further.

There are a number of exceptional breweries in the North East and the regional scene has benefited as a whole from Wylam's development. It's a brother and sisterhood, sharing ideals, friendships, one feeding off another, and engaging with the vision.

It's not just about brewing though; a programme of live music at the brewery is sharpened by an edge of rebellion from the likes of Billy Bragg, The Undertones, Half Man Half Biscuit, and Fish. Paul Simon's Graceland album was performed live by The London African Gospel choir, and local legends Lindisfarne, soul sensation Michael Kiwanuka and DJ sets with Motoon and Mr Scruff have all drawn the crowds. Collaborations with the

> " *It's a brother and sisterhood, all sharing ideals, friendships, one feeding off another and engaging with the vision*

Now well into its stride and with the Grand Hall such a magnificent backdrop, Wylam Brewery hosts weddings, corporate events, festive parties and every occasion in-between, such as the fun food competitions The Battle of the Burger and The Argie Bhaji.

Its annual Craft Beer Calling festival is an assembly of some of the world's best craft beer producers, a three-day extravaganza that reads like a who's who of contemporary brewing – Wild Beer, Brooklyn, Cloudwater, Left-Handed Giant, Beavertown, Siren, Tiny Rebel, Sierra Nevada, North Brewing Company and local progressives such as Almasty and Box Social, along with Wylam's own offerings.

Staff are in constant demand for meet-the-brewer sessions across the country, as well as for tap-takeovers, bar technical services and seminars. Regular brewers' and street food markets are must-visits. An in-house laboratory is under way, while an export strategy is paying off throughout Europe and into the Far East.

The Wylam Brewery trail demonstrates the riches the North East enjoys in a sector that reaches beyond brewing and into tourism, inward investment, culture, entertainment, leisure and job creation.

It hasn't all been easy; Wylam's progression from lowly cattle shed beginnings has been no walk in the park. At the Palace of Arts, however, that's exactly what it is.

new brewing greats offer regular opportunities to share ideas with the likes of Northern Monk, Track Brewing Company, Magic Rock, Brighton Bier, Mad Hatter, Friends of Ham and Simply Hops.

Wylam has developed three ranges of core beers plus an enviable set of one-offs, seasonals and limited editions. The core keg collection includes Hickey The Rake (4.2% abv) limonata pale, the massively complex Jakehead IPA (6.3% abv), and Swipe Right SPA (4.7%) - a super-sippable smashed juice session pale. The core cask range consists of Jakehead IPA (6.3%% abv), Galatia (3.9% abv), Puffing Billy (5.5% abv) smoked black bitter, and the single malt triple hop Cascade (4.1% abv).

Heritage cask beers – old favourites – have benefited from a new lease of life. They are Red Kite (4.5% abv) ruby red "Scotch" ale; Angel (4.3% abv) pale copper ale; the light and soft-bodied Collingwood (4.1% abv); and Gold Tankard (4.0% abv), which includes ingredients with all-gold connotations, such as Golden Promise barley malt.

PALACE OF ARTS, EXHIBITION PARK CLAREMONT ROAD, NEWCASTLE UPON TYNE, NE2 4PZ

📞 **0191 650 0651**

📘 **@WylamBrewery**

🐦 **@wylambrewery**

📷 **@wylam_brewery**

GLOSSARY OF TERMS

A handy guide to some of the words, phrases and abbreviations used in this book that might require clarification.

abv
Alcohol by volume, a measure of the percentage of alcohol in a finished beer.

Aftertaste
The sensation and taste left in the mouth after swallowing a beer which can last for a very short time or linger for quite a while.

Aged ales
Beers set aside, usually in large oak casks, for maturing over a period following primary fermentation.

Alcohol
The main intoxicant in fermented drinks and a waste product of the digestion of sugars by yeast.

Ale
A type of top-fermented beer. Lagers are fermented by yeasts that act at the bottom of a vessel.

Barrel
A 30-gallon cask and not a catch-all name for other sizes. The general name is cask.

Beer
The generic name for a non-distilled alcoholic drink produced by fermentation of a wort derived from mashed malted barley grain.

Bottle-conditioned
A bottled beer where a secondary fermentation takes place due to the yeast left in the mixture.

Brewery tap
A pub built into brewery premises, an area inside a brewery for tasting, or a pub serving almost exclusively one brewery's beers.

CAMRA
Campaign For Real Ale, a consumer group launched in 1971 as a reaction against keg beers produced by large breweries which dominated the marketplace.

Cask
The general name for barrel-shaped containers of any size used for traditional draught beer.

Cask-conditioned
The essence of cask ale; the beer must contain enough yeast for a slow secondary fermentation to produce the subtle flavours that distinguish real ale from filtered, pasteurised keg beer.

Champion Beer of Britain
The highest accolade awarded by CAMRA (the Campaign For Real Ale) at its annual Great British Beer Festival.

Conditioning tanks
Steel vats for conditioning beer. Maintaining condition – enough dissolved carbon dioxide for the beer to be palatable – is a skilled job.

Copper
A brewery vessel in which wort and hops are boiled which will then be transferred to fermentation vessels.

Craft brewery
Relatively small, independently owned commercial breweries employing traditional brewing methods that emphasise flavour and quality.

Fermentation
The biochemical reaction where sugar is converted into ethyl alcohol by yeast which then converts the wort into beer.

Gose
A beer originating in Goslar, Germany, brewed with at least 50% of the grain bill being malted wheat. Flavours include lemon, salt and herbal characteristics.

Grundy tank
UK-built mass-produced pub cellar tanks used in the 1950s and 1960s for storing beer to be pumped to the bar counter after delivery by tanker. The American home-brewing industry bought them up for using at almost every stage of the brewing process due to their versatility.

Home brew
Brewing beer at home for private consumption. This can be from using very basic commercial kits or quite sophisticated equipment and ingredients.

Hop
The tall climbing plant, *humulus lupulus*, that produces the flowers containing aromatic and preserving compounds used in beer primarily as a flavouring and stability agent, to which they impart bitter, zesty, or citric flavours.

IPA
India Pale Ale, originally applied to strong pale ales of high-keeping qualities brewed to come into condition on the long sea voyage to India that would slake the thirsts of British troops stationed there in the 19th Century.

Keg beer
A pressurised brewery-conditioned or processed beer, usually pasteurised, which was originally easy to keep and dispense. Many brewers nowadays produce keg beers that are a world away from their predecessors and retain much of the flavour characteristics of cask ale.

Lager
Beer that's bottom-fermented with the yeast *saccharomyces uvarum* (formerly *saccharomyces carlsbergenes*) at lower temperatures than ales over a longer period of time. The German word lager means store.

Late hopping
The practice of adding aroma hops to a brewing kettle during the last few minutes of the boil to restore flavour and aroma.

Malt
Barley which has been partly germinated then kilned to convert starch into fermentable sugars.

Microbrewery
A small-scale independent brewing operation which can vary substantially in size. In this book, Camerons is the only brewery that would not come under the microbrewery reference.

Mash
To infuse water and malt in the mash tun to extract the fermentable materials from the malt.

Real ale
Beer brewed from traditional ingredients and matured by secondary fermentation in the container from which it is dispensed without the use of extraneous carbon dioxide. The name and definition were coined by CAMRA (the Campaign For Real Ale).

Tap takeover
A brewery serves a range of its beers exclusively in a pub, usually marking a product launch. Also an opportunity to meet brewers and other interested parties.

A-Z Guide

Our at-a-glance guide to the ever-expanding brewing landscape in the North East of England - as of November 2017

ALLENDALE BREWERY
Allen Mill, Allendale, Hexham
Northumberland, NE46 9EA

ALMASTY BREWING CO.
Unit 11, Algernon Industrial Estate
Newcastle upon Tyne, NE27 0NB

ANARCHY BREW CO.
Whitehouse Farm Centre, Morpeth
Northumberland, NE61 6AW

AUTUMN BREWING CO.
8 East Cliff Road, Spectrum Business
Park, Seaham, County Durham
SR7 7PS

BEACON BRAUHAUS
27 Hide Hill, Berwick upon Tweed
Northumberland, TD15 1EQ

BEAR CLAW BREWERY
Unit 334 Meantime Workshops, Spittal
Berwick upon Tweed, Northumberland
TD15 1RG

BIG LAMP BREWERY
Grange Road, Newburn
Newcastle upon Tyne, NE15 8NL

BLACKSTORM BREWERY
York Road, Whitley Bay, Tyne & Wear
NE26 1AB

BOX SOCIAL BREWING
Units 1-3 Winnings Courtyard
Newburn, Newcastle upon Tyne
NE15 9RU

BRINKBURN ST. BREWERY
Quayside i4, Ouseburn Building
Albion Row, Newcastle upon Tyne
NE6 1LL

CAMERONS BREWERY LTD
Lion Brewery, Hartlepool
County Durham, TS24 7QS

CASTLE EDEN BREWERY
8 East Cliff Road, Seaham
County Durham, SR7 7PS

CONSETT ALE WORKS
115 Sherburn Terrace, Consett
County Durham, DH8 6NE

CREDENCE BREWING
16B Coquet Enterprise Park, Amble
Northumberland, NE65 0PE

CULLERCOATS BREWERY
Unit 19, Maurice Road Ind Est
Wallsend, Tyne & Wear, NE28 6BY

DARWIN BREWERY
Unit 1, West Quay Court, Sunderland
Enterprise Park, Sunderland, SR5 2TE

THE DOG & RABBIT BREWERY
36 Park View, Whitley Bay
Tyne & Wear, NE26 2TH

DONZOKO BREWING
Brougham Terrace, Hartlepool
County Durham, TS8 0XT

THE DURHAM BREWERY
6A Bowburn North Ind Est
Bowburn, County Durham, DH6 5PF

ERRANT BREWERY
Arch 19, Forth Street
Newcastle upon Tyne, NE1 3PG

FIREBRICK BREWERY
Units 10-11, Blaydon Business Centre
Cowen Road, Blaydon on Tyne
NE21 5TW

FIRST & LAST BREWERY
The First & Last Brewery, Bird in Bush
Pub, Elsdon, Northumberland
NE19 1AA

FLASH HOUSE BREWING CO.
Unit 1A, Northumberland Street
North Shields, Tyne & Wear, NE30 1DS

**THE GREAT NORTH EASTERN
BREWING CO.**
Unit E, Contract House, Wellington
Road, West Dunston, Gateshead
Tyne & Wear, NE11 9HS

HADRIAN BORDER
Unit 5, The Preserving Works
Newburn Industrial Estate, Shelley
Road, Newcastle upon Tyne, NE15 9RT

HETTON LAW BREWERY
Hetton Law Farm, Lowick, Berwick upon
Tweed, Northumberland, TD15 2UL

HEXHAMSHIRE BREWERY
Dipton Mill Road, Hexham
Northumberland, NE46 1YA

HIGH HOUSE FARM BREWERY
Matfen, Northumberland, NE20 0RG

HOP & CLEAVER BREWERY
44 Sandhill, Newcastle upon Tyne
NE1 3JF

MAXIM BREWERY
1 Gadwall Road, Rainton Bridge
Houghton le Spring, Tyne & Wear
DH4 5NL

MCCOLL'S BREWERY
Unit 4, Randolph Ind Est, Evenwood
Bishop Auckland, County Durham
DL14 9SJ

**MONTAGU ESTATE
CRAFT BREWERY**
13 Braebridge Place, Newcastle upon
Tyne, NE3 4PX

MORDUE BREWERY
D1-D2, Narvik Way, Tyne Tunnel
Trading Est, North Shields
Tyne & Wear, NE29 7XJ

MUCKLE BREWING
3 Bellister Close, Park Village
Haltwhistle, Northumberland, NE49 0HA

NEWCASTLE BREWING LTD
Arch2, Stepney Bank, Ouseburn
Newcastle upon Tyne, NE1 2NP

NORTH BLYTH MICROBREWERY
Wondell Institute, North Blyth
Northumberland, NE24 1SD

NORTHERN ALCHEMY
The Lab, The Cumberland Arms
James Place Street, Newcastle upon
Tyne, NE6 1LD

OUT THERE BREWING CO.
Unit 4, Foundry Lane Ind Est
Newcastle upon Tyne, NE6 1LH

RIGG & FURROW
Acklington Farm Park
Northumberland, NE65 9AA

ROUNDHILL BREWERY
Unit 1, Lagonda Court, Billingham
Stockton on Tees, TS23 4JF

SAINTS ROW BREWING
2 Hawkesbury Mews, Darlington
County Durham, DL3 6RR

THE SHIP INN BREWERY
Low Newton, Northumberland
NE66 3EL

SONNET 43 BREWHOUSE
Durham Road, Coxhoe
County Durham, DH6 4HX

THE STABLES BREWERY
Beamish, Stanley, County Durham
DH9 0YB

**THE STEAM MACHINE
BREWING CO.**
Unit 14, IES Centre, Horndale Avenue
Newton Aycliffe, County Durham
DL5 6DS

STU BREW
Newcastle University Students' Union
Kings Walk, Newcastle upon Tyne
NE1 8QB

THREE BROTHERS BREWING CO.
Unit 4, Clayton Court
Bowesfield Crescent
Stockton on Tees, TS18 3QX

THREE KINGS BREWERY
14/15 Prospect Terrace, North Shields
Tyne & Wear, NE30 1DX

TWICE BREWED BREW HOUSE
Bardon Mill, Hexham
Northumberland, NE47 7AN

TWO BY TWO BREWING
Unit 19, Point Pleasant Ind Est
Wallsend, Tyne & Wear
NE28 6HA

TYNE BANK BREWERY
375 Walker Road
Newcastle upon Tyne, NE6 2AB

THE VILLAGE BREWER
22 Coniscliffe Road, Darlington
County Durham, DL3 7RG

VIP BREWERY ALNWICK
Unit E-F, Hawkhill Ind Est, Alnwick
Northumberland, NE66 3PG

WHITLEY BAY BREWING CO.
1-2 East Parade, Whitley Bay
Tyne & Wear, NE26 1AW

WYLAM BREWERY
Palace of Arts, Exhibition Park
Newcastle upon Tyne, NE2 4PZ

AFTERWORD

Well, here it is, the first book from everyone's favourite publication devoted to pubs, beer and brewing, Cheers. We founded our monthly pub paper back in 2010, when the word microbrewery was still unfamiliar to some, and many of the pleasures of real ale were still reserved for those in the know.

It is with relief that we are able to report that in the years since Cheers first hit pubs throughout the North East of England, not only has the magazine become a must-read for real ale lovers, but there are also a good many more people making our favourite ales, and a good many more serving them.

This book arose from a bar stool conversation among members of the Cheers team, who found themselves, one dark night after a pint or three, considering the growth of craft brewing in the North East of England.

Astounded that they could each name a dozen different brewers, despite the influence of the fine refreshment they had imbibed prior to the conversation, and surprised to find next morning that there really were that many great breweries in one UK region, they decided there was only one thing for it - write a book.

So that's what they did. The editor of Cheers, Alastair Gilmour, spent time with every one of the breweries detailed in this book, and along with the rest of the team, downed more than his fair share of great beer in the name of research. The result is this - the first Great North East Brewery Guide; our tribute to the good men and women who devote their lives to the pursuit of greatness in beer. Is there any finer vocation than theirs? Surely not. Cheers!